Elgar

Elgar

Transport

A VISUAL HISTORY

•**1938** *DUCHESS OF HAMILTON*
STEAM LOCOMOTIVE

•**1910**
ELECTRIC TRAM

•**1969** *APOLLO 11*
SERVICE MODULE

•**1969** *APOLLO 11*
COMMAND MODULE

•**1901**
PADDLE STEAMER
ANTONIO LEMOS

•**1969** *APOLLO 11*
LUNAR EXCURSION
MODULE

•**1909**
BLÉRIOT TYPE XI MONOPLANE

Transport
A VISUAL HISTORY

ANTHONY WILSON

•1988 FERRARI TESTAROSSA

•1939
BISMARCK
BATTLESHIP

c.750
CHINESE BUFFALO CART

•1784
MONTGOLFIER BROTHERS'
FLESSELLES HOT-AIR BALLOON

DORLING KINDERSLEY

LONDON • NEW YORK • STUTTGART

A DORLING KINDERSLEY BOOK

Project Editor Stephen Setford
Art Editor Lester Cheeseman
Managing Editor Helen Parker
Managing Art Editor Peter Bailey
Picture Research Anna Lord
Editorial Researcher Robert Graham
Production Louise Barratt & Ruth Cobb
Editorial Consultant Eryl Davies

First published in Great Britain in 1995 by
Dorling Kindersley Limited, 9 Henrietta Street,
London WC2E 8PS

A CIP catalogue record for this book is available
from the British Library

ISBN 07513 5285 3

Reproduced by Colourscan, Singapore

Printed and bound in Italy by
A. Mondadori Editore, Verona

Contents

Foreword

THE STORY OF TRANSPORT is the story of our ingenuity in devising new ways of moving people and goods from place to place. Transport has been essential to human life for thousands of years: simple carts and boats were as vital to the farming and fishing communities of the past as cars, trains, buses, and aeroplanes are to us today. Because transport affects our day-to-day lives so profoundly, much of this *Visual History* focuses on the everyday means of transport that ordinary people have used and relied upon over the centuries.

Some of the vehicles, craft, and vessels in this book are not typical, but are included because they carried people on famous voyages of exploration – to distant parts of the world, to the depths of the oceans, and even to the Moon. Others have been chosen to show how transport has been adapted for an enormous variety of specialized uses, from battleships and bombers to wage war, to surfboards and roller skates for sport and leisure activities.

Also well-represented here are "famous firsts" – innovations that represent a significant step forward in the history of transport. For any such innovation to be widely adopted, it must first pass several tests: does it work well and reliably, and meet a real need? Is its technology appropriate for the people who will use it, so that they can service and maintain it? Above all, is it cheap enough for plenty of people to afford? In the following pages, you will find some ideas – such as the "penny farthing" bicycle and Concorde – that failed these tests, as well as many more that were outstandingly successful. Among the "milestones" listed in this book are many of the developments in basic technology – new materials, fuels, and engines, for example – that gave rise to improvements in transport and its infrastructure, such as new bridges, tunnels, roads, and railway lines.

I hope that *Transport: A Visual History* will give an insight into a vital area of our lives that we so often take for granted, as well as a flavour of what is to come. If the future of transport is as varied and as exciting as its past, then we have a lot to look forward to.

Anthony Wilson

Anthony Wilson

10,000 BC–AD 1779
Travelling at nature's pace

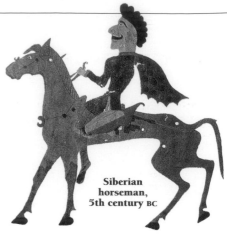

Siberian horseman, 5th century BC

Shoeing horses in northern India, c.AD 1600

FROM THE TIME THE FIRST HUMANS APPEARED half a million years ago, right up to the early 20th century AD, most people lived their lives without ever travelling more than a few miles from where they were born. When they did travel, most of their journeys were made on foot. Even today, the majority of the world's people do not have cars or even bicycles, and seldom travel by bus or train. However, throughout history new methods of transport have had a dramatic influence on the world in which we live. In the period before 2000 BC, there were three particularly important innovations: the hollowed-out boat, the wheeled cart, and horse riding. Together, they shaped the pattern of transport up to the late 18th century AD, and their influence is still felt today.

The birth of the boat

People probably first took to the water on logs or flat rafts made of small branches tied together. These objects float naturally, but they sink if too much weight is loaded aboard. The first "boat-shaped" boats were made by hollowing out tree-trunks. The shape of a hollowed-out boat holds air, so it can carry much more weight than a solid log or raft. By 2500 BC, the Egyptians were building ships from small wooden planks, and equipping them with sails.

HARNESSING HORSE POWER

The horse has played a crucial and varied role in transport through the ages, because it is a fast, strong, hardy animal. Just as cars are made in a variety of shapes and sizes, so people have bred many types of horse, with different qualities to suit different needs. Some were bred to be powerful draught or pack animals, while others were bred for their speed and stamina. The invention of the horseshoe enabled horses to travel over more difficult terrain.

Bronze model of a Roman racing chariot, 2nd century AD

The chariots were light for maximum speed, and sometimes very ornate.

During their racing years, champion stallions were used for breeding.

Spoked wheels

THE CHANGING WORLD: 10,000 BC–AD 1799

Model of Egyptian reed boats with fishing net, c.2000 BC

HUNTING AND FISHING

The earliest people were wanderers, living in small groups and travelling on foot from place to place in search of food. They lived by hunting wild animals, by fishing, and by picking berries and other food from plants. They had to devise ways of dragging or carrying what they had caught, so that they could take it back to share with the rest of their group. They also found that by venturing onto water on simple rafts and floats, they were able to catch more fish.

FARMING

About 10,000 years ago, people began to plant crops. These early farmers no longer needed to roam and hunt, so they were able to settle in one place for many years. As villages grew into towns, transport was needed to bring food from the countryside. Animals were reared for food, but they were also used to carry farm produce on their backs and pull carts and ploughs. People even learned to ride some species, such as the horse and the elephant.

Chinese model of an ox-drawn plough

The trader and traveller Marco Polo on the Silk Road

MERCHANTS AND TRADERS

Eventually, some people became merchants and traders, buying and selling things that other people needed. They used materials such as salt, animal skins, or pieces of gold and silver in the same way we use money today. Eventually, trade routes thousands of kilometres long were established, such as the Silk Road, which ran from China to Persia. Each merchant travelled a few hundred kilometres and then exchanged his goods with the next merchant on the route.

FIGHTING

When communities grew, so did their squabbles. Family arguments turned into tribal battles, and then into wars between rival rulers and nations. Transport was essential to warfare. Armies marched on foot, but needed wagons to carry supplies. Chariots were used to impress and overwhelm the enemy. Warriors on horseback were faster than foot soldiers, and had a better vantage point from which to fight. Later, specialized ships were developed for battles at sea.

Mounted archer, 5th century BC

Over the years, two main types of ship developed: sleek warships powered by teams of rowers, and more rounded cargo vessels powered by sail. Ships continued to grow larger, faster, and more versatile, until, by the 15th and 16th centuries AD, European explorers such as Christopher Columbus and Ferdinand Magellan were venturing to distant parts of the world in their three-masted "square-riggers".

The chariot pole is topped by a decorative ram's head.

Horses, wheels, and carts

People first learned to ride horseback about 4,000 years ago. For anyone who could afford it, a horse provided a form of high-speed personal transport. It also proved invaluable as a "beast of burden" for carrying loads, and as a draught animal for pulling carts and other vehicles.

The earliest carts were unwieldy, and their solid wooden wheels needed a good surface to run on. By 2000 BC, carpenters had learned to build wheels with spokes, which were larger and lighter, and ran better over uneven ground. Over the next 4,000 years, the cart was adapted into a wide variety of chariots, wagons, coaches, and carriages.

By the late 18th century AD, horse-drawn stage coaches were rattling through the towns and cities of several countries, and international trade relied on splendid sailing ships that plied the world's oceans. But transport still depended entirely on animal or wind power, and ships and land vehicles were still built from wood and other natural materials, with only a little metal where it was essential. All this was to change in the years ahead.

THE TECHNOLOGY OF TRANSPORT

BEATING FRICTION

The wheel is the greatest human victory in the battle against friction – the dragging force that makes it hard to slide a heavy object over a rough surface. When a heavy load is moved on wheels, the part of the wheel that touches the ground does not slide but rolls, so there is very little friction there. Instead, there is some friction where the revolving axle rubs against its mount. People soon learned to reduce this friction by putting a leather sleeve between the moving surfaces, and by using greasy animal fat – another important anti-friction device – as a lubricant.

Chinese wheelbarrow

The longer the handles of a wheelbarrow, the less force is needed to lift the load.

Friction at the axle is reduced by lubrication.

No sliding occurs where the wheel touches the ground.

STAYING AFLOAT

If you push an empty bottle down into a bath of water, you can feel the water pushing up against you. The water around the bottle presses on it and holds it up. The ancient Greek scientist Archimedes discovered that the more water an object "displaces", or pushes out of the way, the more strongly it is held up by the water around it. A hollowed-out boat is not only light in itself, but can also carry a heavy cargo, since its shape allows it to displace a lot of water without submerging. And because it holds air, it can even be made of material such as iron, which does not normally float.

The hollow shape makes the boat displace a large amount of water.

North American Indian birchbark canoe

Water presses on the boat to hold it up.

FINDING THE WAY

The first ocean sailors kept close to familiar shores. To help them navigate, they noted the direction of the Sun as it rose and set, the position of the stars at night, and which way the wind was blowing. Later, instruments such as the astrolabe, which measures the height of the Sun or stars above the horizon, were developed. By about AD 1000, some sailors were navigating using simple magnetic compasses.

Astrolabe, AD 1585

EXPLORING THE WORLD

Throughout history, people have ventured far from home to find out about the wonders of the wider world. Others often followed and settled in the places they had visited. Sailors from ancient Greece explored the European and African coasts, setting up colonies. European travellers later reached and settled in the lands now called Australia and America. Ships such as the *Mayflower*, which carried English settlers to America, today seem very small and fragile for such difficult voyages.

Model of the Mayflower, AD 1620

Roman road at Pompeii, Italy

EMPIRES AND ROADS

As nations quarrelled, rulers invaded and conquered neighbouring countries, sometimes creating huge empires. They included the empires of Egypt, Persia, and Rome, and the Mayas of Central America. To rule such large areas, networks of roads were set up, so that messengers on horseback could bring news from distant parts in just a few days. Roads also enabled armies to move quickly to trouble-spots, and made trade within the empire much easier.

CANALS FOR TRADE

The easiest way to move goods from one place to another was often by boat. Where there was no suitable river, a channel was dug and filled with water to make a canal along which barges could be towed by people or animals. The Egyptians built their first canal more than 4,000 years ago, while the Chinese started work on their Grand Canal in about 500 BC. Canals did not become important trade routes in Europe until medieval times.

Painting of the Grand Canal, China, 18th century AD

10,000 BC

5000 BC

10,000 BC	9000 BC	8000 BC	7000 BC	6000 BC	5000 BC	4600 BC	4200 BC	3800 BC

LAND

Before 10,000 BC TRANSPORT ON FOOT

For early people, the only way to travel over land was on foot. Only young children and the sick or injured would get a lift, carried by stronger members of the group. A heavy load, such as a large animal caught for food, would have to be dragged along the ground, or carried on a person's back. A very heavy animal might be slung from a wooden pole, so that its weight was shared by several people.

Stone Age hunter carrying his kill

Reconstruction of a sledge from a royal tomb in Ur, Mesopotamia, c.2700–2400 BC

Runner

c.5000 BC SLEDGES

As an alternative to carrying heavy objects, people learned to drag them along on pieces of animal skin or tree bark. From this, they developed the wooden sledge. In Mesopotamia (now part of Iraq), large sledges were used for moving statues or blocks of stone. Smaller ones may have been used by royalty as a kind of chariot. Adding ski-like "runners" beneath the sledge reduced friction with the ground, making it easier to pull. *See* VIKING SLEDGE C.AD 850.

c.5000 BC PACK ANIMALS

The first domesticated animals were kept for food or, like the dog, to help with hunting. The ass, a member of the horse family similar to a donkey, was probably the first species to be used as a "pack animal" – that is, for carrying a load. Asses can carry up to 60 kg (130 lb).

Egyptian procession, showing tame ass as pack animal

c.4000 BC WOODEN ROLLERS

To build religious and astronomical monuments, people in Europe may have moved huge stone building blocks using rollers made from tree-trunks. The stones, called "megaliths", were first transported from quarries by boat. Rollers were then placed beneath them, and they were hauled overland to the building site.

Moving a megalith using wooden rollers

WATER

Log raft from Western Australia

c.10,000 BC LOGS AND RAFTS

The first water transport was probably simply a floating log or tree-trunk. Later, people learned to lay a number of branches, or bundles of reeds, side by side and bind them together to make a raft. The raft was controlled by paddling with arms or legs, but people soon discovered that a flat piece of wood makes a better paddle. To carry more weight, floats were attached around the edge of the raft.

Pitch-covered quffa from Iran

Assyrian carving of man fishing astride an inflated animal skin

c.10,000 BC ANIMAL-SKIN FLOATS

To keep them – and their rafts – afloat, people learned how to take the skin of an animal, stitch up the holes, and blow it up like an air cushion. To cross a deep river, they lay across the inflated skin and paddled with their arms and legs. Large pots and gourds were also used as floats.

c.7000 BC DUG-OUTS

"Dug-outs" – the first real boats – were made by burning the wood from inside one half of a split tree-trunk, or gouging it out with stone tools. A hollowed-out boat can carry more weight than a raft and is easier to steer. Other early boats were made from strips of tree bark. *See* BARK CANOE AD 1770.

Making a dug-out

c.5000 BC SKIN BOATS

Since early times, animal skins have been used as waterproof coverings for boats. The skins were sewn together and stretched over a frame of wooden branches or basket-work. Later basket-boats, such as the round quffas and coracles, were waterproofed with pitch – a black material obtained from tar. Quffas, used on the River Euphrates in Babylon more than 2,000 years ago, can still be seen today.

Steering oar

c.3100 BC SAILING BOAT *Egypt*

The first sailing boats were probably made by the ancient Egyptians. They found that with a square sail, the power of the wind could be harnessed on journeys up the River Nile, because the wind usually blows in the upstream direction in Egypt. On the return trip downstream, the boat was either paddled or allowed to drift along with the current, steered by a long oar at the back.

The boat is steered from the back, or "stern".

Model of an Egyptian sailing boat, c.1800 BC

The boat's owner sits beneath an ox-hide canopy.

MILESTONES

•**10,000 BC** Hunter-gatherer people from Asia spread into North America through Alaska. Eventually, they will spread as far down as the tip of South America, but their rate of progress is slow – only about 16 km (10 miles) a year.

•**10,000 BC** The wolf is the first wild animal to be tamed, or "domesticated", becoming the dog. Later, dogs will be used to pull sledges and carts.

•**8000 BC** A paddle found at Star Carr in Yorkshire, England, is the earliest archaeological evidence of water transport, showing that people living beside a lake there are using boats.

•**8000 BC** People from mainland Greece travel 120 km (75 miles) by sea to the island of Melos to gather obsidian, a glassy stone used to make cutting tools. This is the earliest known long-distance sea voyage.

•**7500 BC** Farming begins in southwest Asia. To transport their crops, farmers will eventually need carts or sledges, and tamed animals to pull them.

•**6000 BC** Boats are in use for deep-sea fishing off the coasts of Scotland and Sweden in northern Europe.

Reconstruction of early plank wheel

•**5000 BC** Sledges are used to move people and goods over snow, sand, and grassland.

•**5000 BC** Pack animals such as asses are used to carry loads. Other early pack animals are donkeys, camels, and elephants in Asia, and llamas in South America.

•**4500 BC** Horses are tamed for the first time, either in the grasslands, or "steppes", of the Ukraine, or in what is now Turkey or Iran. They are later used as pack animals.

•**3500 BC** Wheeled vehicles are in use in Mesopotamia. The first one may have been a sledge to which four wheels were added.

•**3500 BC** Roads are built in Mesopotamia to help traders move between villages, towns, and cities. Simple bridges of stone slabs help people to cross streams.

•**3100 BC** Ships with sails appear on the River Nile in Egypt. These ships are made from bundles of papyrus, a tall reed-like plant.

3000 BC

2000 BC

3000 BC	2800 BC	2600 BC	2400 BC	2200 BC	2000 BC	1800 BC	1600 BC	1400 BC	1200 BC

c.3000 BC HORSE-RIDING

In ancient times, horses roamed wild in many parts of the world. One of the most important developments in the history of transport came when people first learned to ride horseback – probably about 5,000 years ago. Horses were personal transport, used for going on journeys, for hunting, and in warfare. Later, the harness was developed to give the rider greater control. It consisted of a bridle (straps fitting around the head) and bit (a metal piece in the mouth).

The ropes supporting the mast and sail are called "rigging".

The sail hangs from a wooden beam called a "yard".

Armoured breastplate

Assyrian warrior riding horse with harness, 7th century BC

c.2400 BC COVERED WAGON *Syria*

The first carts and wagons had many uses. Some belonged to royalty, others to ordinary people, called nomads, who had no fixed homes and lived in covered wagons or in tents. Traders also used covered wagons, similar to this small pottery model, to transport goods they had made for selling as they moved from town to town.

Pottery model of covered wagon, Syria, c.2500–2300 BC

Tutankhamun's war chariot, c.1340 BC

c.1340 BC TWO-WHEELED CHARIOT *Egypt*

Lightweight, two-wheeled chariots may have originated in Sumeria around 2500 BC. Pulled by horses, they were fast and easy to manoeuvre, making them useful in warfare for a surprise attack against foot soldiers. Later Egyptian chariots, such as King Tutankhamun's, had spoked wheels, which are much lighter than solid wheels made from wooden planks. War chariots usually carried two people, one to drive the chariot and the other to fight.

c.2500 BC FOUR-WHEELED CHARIOT *Mesopotamia*

The first wheeled vehicles may have been made in about 3500 BC by the Sumerian people of Mesopotamia. The earliest chariots probably had four wheels, and were pulled by pairs of animals such as onagers – smaller relations of wild horses. The wheels were made of shaped wooden planks, joined by wooden cross-pieces.

Four-wheeled Sumerian war chariot, c.2500 BC

Early sails were made of papyrus, and later, linen.

Men with poles push the boat off sandbanks or away from the shore.

c.2600 BC ROYAL BARGE *Egypt*

Some Egyptian ships, such as the magnificent barge made for King Khufu in about 2600 BC, were purely for ceremonial use. Built mainly of imported cedar wood, the barge was 43 m (141 ft) long and 6 m (20 ft) wide. When Khufu was buried at Giza in the Great Pyramid, his barge was dismantled and buried in a pit nearby, to help him on his journey to the afterlife.

Khufu's royal cabin

Wooden framework for canopy

Khufu's boat had five pairs of oars, which give more power than paddles because they are much longer.

Single mast near the front of the boat

The boat's front is called the "prow".

Model of Khufu's royal barge, c.2600 BC

Sails made of palm leaves

c.2000 BC DOUBLE CANOE *Polynesia*

Four thousand years ago, Polynesian people set out from the islands of Southeast Asia to colonize other Pacific islands. They travelled great distances by raft or canoe. By placing two dug-out canoes side by side and linking them with a deck, they made larger craft that were stable enough to carry sails without capsizing.

Polynesian sailing craft, made of two linked dug-outs

Plumbline to test the depth of the water

The body, or "hull", was made of short wooden planks fixed side by side.

2000–1001 BC

- **3000 BC** In Mesopotamia, the yoke – a wooden board placed across the shoulders – is used so that oxen can pull heavy wagons.
- **3000 BC** People start to ride horses. They probably ride bare-back, and control the horse with a rope tied around its lower jaw.
- **2500 BC** Swimmers in Egypt can do the crawl stroke as well as the breast-stroke.

- **2500 BC** The Egyptians build boats made from short wooden planks.
- **2500 BC** Remains found in Khazakstan show that people are using snow skis.
- **2500 BC** A stone causeway, or raised road, 1 km (0.6 mile) long is built in Egypt over 10 years. Two million huge stones are dragged along it on sledges to build the Great Pyramid.
- **2500 BC** Warriors in Mesopotamia now have four-wheeled war chariots. The nomadic Hyksos people introduce faster, two-wheeled chariots to Egypt nearly 1,000 years later.
- **2300 BC** Canals are dug in Egypt, so that ships can bypass the rapids on the River Nile at Aswan.

- **2000 BC** Roads are built on the island of Malta. They have grooves cut into them 1.3 m (4.3 ft) apart, forming a sort of "railway" along which carts can be pulled.
- **2000 BC** Spoked wheels are used on vehicles in Mesopotamia. They reach Egypt by 1600 BC, and China by 1300 BC.
- **1900 BC** Work starts on the first long-distance "roads" in Europe. These tracks, linking northern Europe with the Mediterranean region, are a trade route for valuable materials such as tin and amber.

- **1400 BC** Wheeled vehicles are now in use in Europe, and spoked wheels are introduced there around 1000 BC.
- **1300 BC** Horse-riders are now controlling their horses using a bit – a jointed metal band that fits inside the horse's mouth and is attached to the horse's headgear, or bridle.
- **1100 BC** Phoenician sailors learn to use the position of the stars to help them navigate their ships at night. They make star maps, and use the North Star to find north.

Early metal horse bit

1000 BC

| 1000 BC | 900 BC | 800 BC | 700 BC | 600 BC | | 200 BC |

Toy camel from Roman Egypt

c.550 BC RACING CHARIOT *Greece*

Drawn by four galloping horses abreast, the Greek racing chariot was powerful but hard to control and liable to skid on bends. In the Olympic Games, up to 40 chariots started the 14-km (9-mile) race, but spills and collisions were frequent, and few reached the finishing line. The prize went to the winning chariot's owner, not its driver.

Greek vase painting showing chariot racing, 6th century BC

Cover made of woven bamboo

Chinese bullock cart

c.1000 BC CAMEL *Middle East*

In hot regions where there were no roads, and where food and water were scarce, the camel proved a more versatile means of transport than the horse. Camels were first used for riding and as pack animals in the Middle East. Later, as more of the Sahara turned to sand, they were introduced into Africa, where long "caravans" of camels carried trading goods across the desert.

c.450 BC FOUR-HORSE CHARIOT *Persia*

Some chariots were fitted with larger wheels, because they gave a smoother ride over rough ground. Studs were sometimes attached around the rims of the wheels to make them less likely to slip. An exquisite gold model found near the River Oxus in central Asia shows a large-wheeled chariot pulled by four small horses attached to two poles.

Wheel strengthened to carry heavy loads

Triremes were crewed by up to 170 oarsmen in three tiers.

The oarsmen sat side-on, along the length of the ship.

Each oarsman rowed with a single oar.

Gold model of a Persian chariot, 5th century BC

c.400 BC NOMADS' CART *Siberia*

The nomadic people who lived in the "steppes", or grasslands, of central Asia used huge carts to carry their belongings as they moved from one place to another. When they stopped to set up camp, the top portion could be lifted down to form the framework of a tent.

Cart from Pazyryk, Siberia, 5th century BC

Cutaway model of a Greek trireme

The two upper rows of oars were nearly 5 m (16 ft) long.

c.500 BC TRIREME *Greece*

By 800 BC, the Phoenicians were building biremes – fast, powerful galleys with two rows of oars on each side. They were followed by triremes, with three rows of oars on each side. By 500 BC, Greek triremes were up to 40 m (130 ft) long. A pointed ram fixed to the "prow", or front, of the ship at the water-line was used to sink enemy ships by smashing a hole in their hulls. Triremes also carried archers and soldiers for boarding other vessels.

The wheels were 1.6 m (5 ft) across.

The lateen is called a "fore-and-aft sail", because it runs along the boat from front to back.

The helmsman guided the boat using two long "tillers" attached to the steering oars.

c.200 BC LATEEN-RIGGED CRAFT *Mediterranean region*

The rectangular sails of early ships ran from side to side. Such sails were of little use if the wind was not blowing in roughly the direction the ship had to go. Triangular "lateen" sails, running along the line of a ship from front to back, enabled ships to sail almost into the wind. Lateen sails first appeared in the Mediterranean region, and are still common on small ships called "dhows".

c.1000 BC TRADING SHIP *Phoenicia*

By 1200 BC, warships and trading ships had begun to look very different. Warships, or "galleys", were long, sleek, and low, powered by oarsmen as well as a sail. Trading ships were broader and deeper, and relied almost entirely on their sails. From 2000–350 BC, the Phoenicians were the most important traders in the Mediterranean. From their base at the eastern end of the Mediterranean (now Syria, Lebanon, and Israel), their wooden trading ships journeyed as far as northern Europe and Africa's west coast.

Sailors climbed the mast to look out for land.

The ship had a single, central mast with a square sail.

Cutaway of a Phoenician trading ship

Model dhow with lateen rigging

The cargo was lashed into place below deck.

The hull was made watertight by coating it with tar.

1000–501 BC

•**1000 BC** The Chinese now have a network of roads with speed limits and officials to keep control. There are traffic regulations about how large vehicles can be, and who has priority at busy crossings.

•**1000 BC** Three thousand years before the first aeroplane, a Greek legend describes how Daedalus and Icarus try to escape from prison by making themselves wings from feathers fastened with thread and wax. Icarus flies too close to the Sun: the wax melts and he falls to his death. Daedalus lands safely in Sicily.

•**1000 BC** The Chinese begin to fly kites. Some are said to be so large that they can lift people into the air.

•**600 BC** In forested and wetland regions of Britain where the ground is soft, people lay down pieces of wood to build "trackways". This provides a firm surface for people and horses.

The Pharos at Alexandria

500–1 BC

•**500 BC** The Royal Road, a levelled track, runs for 2,600 km (1,600 miles) across the Persian empire, from Sardis (in what is now Turkey) to Susa (in Iran). Horseback messengers can travel the whole distance in nine days.

•**500 BC** A trade route later called the Silk Road is established, crossing Asia and linking China with Persia. Along it, merchants carry precious metals and stones, spices, glass, and pottery, as well as silk. Chinese inventions, such as paper and gunpowder, will eventually spread to Europe along this route, as will epidemics of infectious diseases.

•**400 BC** There are about 300 ports dotted around the coast of the Mediterranean Sea, used by fishermen and traders.

•**250 BC** The world's first large lighthouse, the Pharos, is completed at Alexandria in Egypt. The light of a fire burning at the top of this 120-m (400-ft) high tower guides sailors safely into port at night.

•**200 BC** Lateen-rigged sailing ships appear in the Mediterranean region.

•**55 BC** Roman soldiers build a 550-m (1,800-ft) long wooden bridge across the River Rhine in 10 days.

LAND

WATER

MILESTONES

0

AD 500

| 0 | 100 | 200 | 300 | 400 | 500 | 600 | 700 | 800 | 900 |

c.0 BULLOCK CART *China*
Until 2,000 years ago, two-wheeled carts had a single pole, or shaft, at the front. Animals were attached in pairs, one either side of the pole, to pull the cart. The Chinese then began to build carts with two front shafts, enabling them to be pulled by a single animal. The animal stood between the shafts, and a wooden cross-piece called a yoke fitted over its shoulders.

Yoke fits over the bullock's shoulders

Bullock stands between the two shafts

Indian cart with oxen yoked to a central shaft

c.100 SADDLED HORSE *China*
Early horse riders would often throw a piece of cloth over a horse's back before mounting, but it was the Chinese who developed the first saddles, which made riding easier and safer. Made of stiff material such as leather, they were padded and shaped for comfort. Metal stirrups, which fit around the rider's feet, were also in use in China by this time.

Padded saddle   *Harness*

Chinese terracotta horse of the Tang era (AD 610–906)

Model of a Roman corbita, c.2nd century AD

Heraldic device

Cargo hold

A small fore sail, hanging from a forward-leaning mast, made the ship easier to steer.

Anchor

c.0 CORBITA *Rome*
A fleet of sturdy, two-masted ships called "corbitas" sailed between the ports of the Roman empire. To make room for cargo, corbitas had pear-shaped hulls, broader towards the "stern", or back, of the boat. The largest Roman ships carried more than 1,000 tonnes of cargo, such as corn and wine, as well as large numbers of passengers. Some corbitas travelled as far as India.

Viking sledge c.AD 850

A carved beechwood box, decorated with metal studs, was tied to the frame.

Curved oak runners

c.850 VIKING SLEDGE
Scandinavia
The Vikings found that journeys over rugged terrain were often easiest in winter, when snow covered uneven ground. Towed by horses, dogs, reindeer, or people on skis, a sledge's runners glide easily over snow and ice, making it more efficient than a wheeled vehicle.

The decorated spiral "stempost" above the prow is carved into a snake's head.

The raised prow stops the ship from nose-diving into the water in rough weather.

Arab horseman

c.700 ARAB HORSE
Arab influence spread far and wide as the Islamic empire expanded in the 7th and 8th centuries. Camels were the main form of transport, but horses were treasured possessions because of their speed and grace. They were used for fighting, sports, and hunting. Horses were very carefully chosen for breeding, in order to produce high-quality offspring. Arab horses are small, tough, and intelligent, with a silky coat of hair.

Model of a Viking knarr, or trading ship

c.850 VIKING SHIPS *Norway*
The Vikings were intrepid sailors who even ventured across the Atlantic in their open ships. Viking fighting vessels, or long-ships, were narrow and swift, carrying up to sixty oarsmen on each side. Longships, or "karvs", were also used for coastal travel. The karv found at Oseberg, Norway, was 21 m (70 ft) long and was buried in the grave of a wealthy woman – perhaps a queen. Viking trading boats, or "knarrs", were broader, and travelled mainly under sail with a much smaller crew. Their shallow hulls enabled them to travel far up rivers. Knarrs carried Viking settlers as far as Iceland and Greenland.

Reconstruction of the Oseberg Viking ship, 9th century AD

Oar ports

"Clinker" hull of overlapping planks held together by iron rivets.

The bottom of the hull is strengthened by a projecting backbone of timbers called a "keel".

• **0–100** The Romans use horseshoes consisting of metal plates tied under a horse's hooves with strips of leather.
• **0–300** The padded saddle and the rigid stirrup are invented in China, along with the padded collar, which allows horses to pull heavier loads without choking themselves.
• **0–400** Eighty thousand kilometres (50,000 miles) of straight roads are built to link the cities of the Roman empire.
• **100** Chariot racing in Rome attracts crowds of up to 250,000 people. Bets are placed, and winning charioteers become popular heroes.
• **100** The rudder is in use on Chinese ships by now, but may have been invented earlier.

• **200** Metal ice-skates are used in Scandinavia. Earlier skates may have been made of bone splinters strapped to leather boots.
• **250** The Maya civilization in Central America reaches its greatest development, but without the aid of pack animals or wheeled vehicles. Maya traders transport their goods on their backs or by canoe.
• **250** The Chinese invent the wheelbarrow. It reaches Europe 1,000 years later.

• **605** Work is completed on the first sections of China's Grand Canal. The canal will eventually be more than 1,000 km (600 miles) long, linking the Yangtse River with the north of the country. By the 8th century, ships on the canal will carry 2 million tonnes of goods each year.
• **875–985** The Vikings set out from Scandinavia in their longships to start settlements in Iceland and Greenland.

Viking boot and skate, 10th century AD

• **900** Iron horseshoes, which are nailed onto a horse's hooves, are widely used throughout Europe. They were probably developed at an earlier date by the Romans or the Celts.
• **984** Locks are used for the first time on China's Grand Canal. A lock is a compartment with a gate at each end that allows a barge to pass from a higher level of a canal to a lower level, and vice versa.

1000

1175

| 1000 | 1035 | 1070 | 1105 | 1175 | 1210 | 1245 | 1280 | 1315 |

LAND

c.1000 WARHORSE *Japan*
Japanese samurai warriors wore very light armour, so they were able to ride swift, light horses from the mountains of northern Japan. Samurai were expert horsemen, able to fire arrows accurately from a fast-moving horse. Later, European knights wore thicker, heavier metal armour into battle, which prevented the horses from moving fast. In fact, horses often wore armour as well, so they had to be large and strong enough to carry up to 180 kg (400 lb).

The horse wears a colourful coat decorated with heraldic designs.

Chain-mail armour

Reconstruction of a jousting knight, 14th century

Early samurai warrior

c.1200 WARHORSE *Europe*
Strength and steadiness were essential for both horse and knight in battle. These were acquired in a sport called jousting, which was also good battle training. Pairs of armoured knights rode full-tilt towards one another, each with the aim of breaking his lance (a long, spear-like weapon) against his opponent's shield, or knocking him off his horse.

Farm cart with studded wheels, c.1340

c.1340 TWO-WHEELED CART *Europe*
Early harnesses tended to throttle horses if they pulled too hard when towing carts and wagons. By the 14th century, harnesses with padded collars were in common use in Europe, allowing horses to pull much harder without such danger. Cart wheels often had metal rims, called tyres, as well as studs to prevent them from slipping sideways.

The sails are made of matting.

Most junks are three-masted, but larger ones have five.

The light armour was made of small, thin, iron plates, lacquered and laced together with silk and leather.

Four-sided "lugsails" hang from the masts at an angle.

Fighting cog, 1340

WATER

The sails are stiffened with bamboo strips, keeping them flat and making it easy to fold up part of a sail in high winds.

c.1000 JUNK *China*
Flat-bottomed boats called "junks" were developed in China more than 1,000 years ago. They were strongly built for sailing on the open seas of eastern Asia, and were used for both trading and fighting. At the stern they had a rudder, a flat plate under the boat that cuts through the water. The invention of the rudder was crucial to the development of larger ships, which could not be steered properly with oars.

The ship is steered by swivelling the "sternpost" rudder.

Model of a five-masted junk

The broad, flat hull has no keel.

Square bow

1340 COG *Europe*
Cogs were tubby, single-masted ships that served both as cargo vessels and as warships. Their two "castles" – raised areas at the prow and the stern – made them easier to defend. Steered by a rudder and with a clinker-built hull (made from overlapping planks), sturdy cogs could withstand the rough North Atlantic seas.

MILESTONES

1000–1174			1175–1349	

•**1000** Wagons are built with a pivoted cross-bar at the front called a "whippletree", to which harnesses are attached. It allows a team of horses to share the pulling of a wagon.
•**1002** Sailing west from Greenland, Norseman Leif Ericsson becomes the first European to visit North America.
•**1010** Oliver of Malmesbury, an English monk, jumps from a tower with wings on his hands and feet. He does not fly, but breaks his legs.

Chinese mariner's compass

•**1040** The recipe for "Black Powder" (gunpowder) rocket fuel is published in China.
•**1100s** The Incas of South America start to build two roads, totalling 6,400 km (4,000 miles), to link parts of their empire. No wheeled vehicles will ever use these roads, just animals and people.
•**1119** Chinese sailors navigate with a "south-pointing needle" – a compass made of a magnetized piece of iron floating in water. The iron turns to show magnetic north.

•**1187** Sailors in Europe are now using the magnetic compass.
•**1200** The sternpost rudder begins to appear on European ships, although it has been used before now on Chinese and Byzantine vessels.
•**1250** Roger Bacon, an English monk, writes a book in which he speculates about hollow globes that float in the air (balloons) and mechanical flying machines propelled by people riding on them.
•**1250** Single-masted sailing ships called cogs begin to appear in European waters.
•**1271** Seventeen-year-old Marco Polo from Venice sets out with his father and uncle on a journey across Asia that will last 24 years.

Wooden wing frame with netting support, perhaps for a covering of birds' feathers

•**1280** The Mediterranean lateen sail is now in use on European vessels.
•**1290** Marco Polo sees four-masted Chinese junks in China; ten years later he sees man-carrying kites in China.

1350   1525

| 1350 | 1385 | 1420 | 1455 | 1490 | 1525 | 1560 | 1595 | 1630 |

c.1550 SNOWSHOES *Scandinavia*
People in cold countries learned to attach showshoes to their boots – and even to their animals' hooves – when walking on soft snow. Similar in shape and size to tennis rackets, snowshoes spread a person's weight and stop their feet from sinking into the snow.

Man and pack horse wearing snowshoes, c.1550

1565·
LITTER *Peru*
A litter is a portable couch supported by long poles and carried by animals or by human bearers. Litters were important in Peru, because the Inca people had no wheeled vehicles. They were also widely used in Europe before comfortable wheeled coaches were available.

Litter carrying Inca emperor, 1565

Elephant armour, c.1600

1560·
STATE COACH *England*
In 1560, England's Queen Elizabeth I started a fashion when she acquired her own state coach. Soon, many other important women wanted their own luxury vehicles. Before this, royalty and wealthy people made journeys in bumpy "travelling carriages", which were little more than covered farm wagons.

Replica of Elizabeth I's state coach, 1560

c.1600 ARMOURED ELEPHANT *India*
Because of their strength and size, elephants have been used in warfare since the time of Alexander the Great in the 4th century BC, and possibly before. They were sent into battle to terrify enemy troops and trample on them. In India, they wore armour made of metal plates sewn onto a cloth backing.

Royal flag of Spain

The Santa Maria was probably a "carrack", a small ship with three masts.

•1511 WARSHIP *Europe*
The age of great sea battles in Europe started with the development of gun-carrying warships, later called "galleons". They had rows of guns on either side, placed low down to stop them from being top-heavy and liable to capsize. The guns were fired through holes cut into the ship's hull.

The English warship Mary Rose, built in 1511

c.1562 GONDOLA *Venice*
There were 10,000 gondolas in Venice in the 16th century, carrying people around a city that has canals in place of streets. Today, there are far fewer of these sleek wooden boats, but they are still propelled by "gondoliers" who stand at the stern to operate a single long oar. According to a law passed in 1562, all gondolas must be painted black.

Stern oar

The metal fitting at the bow may have developed from a ram.

Venetian gondola

•1492 SANTA MARIA *Spain*
Christopher Columbus led his expedition across the Atlantic in a 25-m (80-ft) long ship called *Santa Maria*. Knowing that the Earth is round, Columbus aimed to reach the Far East by sailing westwards from Europe. After more than a month at sea, land was sighted. However, this was not an Eastern land, but a "New World" unknown to people in Europe. It was later called America.

Model of the Santa Maria, 1492

•1620 SUBMARINE *England*
Several inventors tried to devise simple submarines. One of them was Cornelius Drebbel, a Dutchman working in London. It is claimed that his "diving boat" successfully travelled several miles up the River Thames in London. It was rowed by twelve oarsmen who were supplied with air through tubes from the surface.

Wooden submarine, 1683

| 1350–1524 | 1525–1699 |

"Ornithopter" based on the drawings of Leonardo da Vinci

•**1420** Henry the Navigator, a Portuguese prince, inspires sailors to explore the coast of Africa.
•**1492** Christopher Columbus makes the first of his four journeys to Central America and the Caribbean.
•**1497–8** From Portugal, Vasco da Gama sails around Africa to India.
•**1505** In Italy, Leonardo da Vinci starts a study of flight and makes drawings of flying machines.
•**1519** Hernando Cortés takes at least 16 horses from Spain to Mexico. Horses have been extinct on the American continent for 8,000 years.
•**1522** Ferdinand Magellan's *Vittoria* is the first ship to complete a round-the-world voyage.

•**1350–1450** Three-masted "carrack" ships slowly replace the smaller cogs. *See* COG 1340.
•**1400** Wagons appear that have a body hung from the chassis, or main framework, by leather straps, giving a more comfortable ride.

•**1538** Primitive diving bells are used in Spain.
•**1550** High-sided ships called "galleons" are common in Europe. They are used as both fighting and trading ships.
•**1550** European noblemen are acquiring their own road vehicles, called "coaches" after the Hungarian town of Kocs.
•**1600** A programme of road building starts in France. By 1664, the roads will be so good that a stage coach service starts.
•**1600** About 600 carriages are available for hire in London, and 300 in Paris. In London, they are called "hackneys".

•**1640** "Sedans" – enclosed chairs carried by two bearers – are popular in many European cities.
•**1650** A three-wheeled invalid carriage, with "pedals" turned by hand, is used by a disabled man, Stephen Farfler, in Nuremberg, Germany.
•**1662** A horse-drawn bus service starts in Paris, with set routes and timetables.
•**1675** Greenwich Observatory is set up near London. Its services will help seamen throughout the world to navigate better.

1700

1720

LAND

c.1700 HORSEBACK WARRIOR *Nigeria*
In tropical Africa, the easiest way to travel was by river. For land travel, horses could not be used because they were attacked by the tsetse fly, which carried a fatal disease. This Benin warrior came from a part of Nigeria where the tsetse fly was rare, and the ruler kept an army that included many horsemen.

Bronze plaque of mounted Benin warrior, c.1700

c.1700 STAGE WAGON *England*
Lumbering stage wagons ran regularly on important cross-country routes, carrying a few passengers as well as several tonnes of goods. Ten or twelve horses were needed to pull these huge vehicles, which sometimes covered as much as 32 km (20 miles) a day in good weather. Stage wagons had broad wheels to stop them from sinking into mud, and were controlled by "drovers" who walked or rode alongside.

Stage wagon

c.1720 SEDAN CHAIR *Europe*
To beat traffic jams, wealthy people hired sedan chairs instead of coaches. Carried by two "chairmen", a sedan could go through streets too narrow for a coach. Sedans were also used on longer journeys. They were often elaborately decorated outside and luxurious within.

Wooden frame

Sedan chair, c.1720

Skin bag decorated with beads

North American Indian cradle-board, c.1850

Coal-carrying wagonway

c.1730 WAGONWAY *Europe*
The first "railways" were wooden planks or metal plates laid down so that horses could pull wagons more easily. In the example above, a full wagon coasts downhill, controlled by a driver sitting on the brake lever. The horse will pull the wagon back up for the next load. A horse might also pull a full wagon uphill, then ride back down in an empty one.

•1735 TRANSPORT FOR CHILDREN
For his children, the Duke of Devonshire built a tiny carriage that could be pulled by a dog, goat, or pony. Baby carriages were later called "perambulators" or "prams". But throughout history, most babies were carried on their mothers' backs in animal-skin pouches. A cradle-board, used by North American Indians, was a skin bag on a frame. It was strapped to the mother's back, hung from a saddle, or tied to a travois. *See* TRAVOIS c.1880.

Child's carriage made for Duke of Devonshire

WATER

Single square sail

Model of a Japanese cargo vessel

c.1700 CARGO SHIP *Japan*
From 1639 to 1858, the Japanese government tried to preserve the country's culture and religion by banning all contact with the outside world. People were not allowed to leave the country, and the size of cargo ships was restricted so that they could not be sailed to foreign lands. The square-rigged vessel above had an opening in the stern, into which the rudder was raised if the ship was at anchor. Similar ships were still being built early in the 20th century.

Masts were made taller by adding extensions called "topmasts".

The masts are supported at the sides by ladder-like arrangements of ropes called "shrouds".

Mizzen mast

Main mast

Fore mast

The supporting ropes running fore and aft are called "stays".

Bowsprit

•1733 WARSHIP *Europe*
In the 18th century, the galleon grew into a floating fortress. A large warship, called a "First-Rate" ship, had 100 guns, a crew of 850, and displaced 3,000 tonnes of water. Warships also carried more sails, supported by a forest of rigging. This made them faster and more manoeuvrable. In the Mediterranean Sea, galleys similar to those of ancient Greece could still be seen. Their many oarsmen enabled them to attack becalmed sailing boats, which could not escape when there was no wind. *See* WARSHIP 1511.

Fourth-Rate ship, 1733–1850

Maltese galley, c.1770

•1700 Ships known as East Indiamen bring valuable cargoes of ivory, spice, and silk from India, China, and the East Indies, into European ports.
•1710 Larger ships are now steered by turning a wheel on the deck. This is linked to a mechanism called a block and tackle, which moves the rudder.
•1712 The first steam engine, of the type devised by Thomas Newcomen, starts working in England, where it is used to pump water from coal mines. After improvements by James Watt and others, coal-powered steam engines will revolutionize land and sea transport.

A Fourth-Rate ship carried 50–70 guns (later 60–80) that mainly fired solid round shot made of iron.

•1714 The British government offers a £20,000 prize for the first ship's clock that keeps accurate time at sea. The prize is won by John Harrison, with his No. 4 chronometer of 1759.
•1716 The French establish the first national highways department.
•1717 English astronomer Edmond Halley develops a diving bell with a system for refreshing the air in the bell.

The capstan – a large drum turned by spoke-like poles – was used to wind in the anchor or raise the yards.

John Harrison's 1759 No. 4 chronometer

•1730s Wheels made from cast iron – a hard brittle metal – start to replace wooden ones on wagonways in Europe. Steam trains will later rely on all-metal wheels.
•1731 In Philadelphia, a hand-operated pump is used to put out fires, instead of a chain of water-filled buckets. Mounted on wheels, it is the first practical fire engine in the USA.

•1731 Englishman John Hadley invents the octant, which gives latitude at sea by measuring the height of the Sun or stars above the horizon.
•1732 In England, the first "lightship" is anchored near the mouth of the River Thames. A lightship is an alternative to a lighthouse where it is not possible to build foundations. *See* LIGHTSHIP 1963.
•1735 Swiss engineer Charles Dangeau de Labelye develops the "caisson". This box-like shell can be lowered onto a riverbed and the water pumped out from inside, enabling engineers to build bridge foundations "underwater".

1740

1760

c.1740 POST-CHAISE *France/England*
The lightweight "chaise de poste" carriage was first made in France in the 1660s. It was introduced to England in 1743, where it was called the post-chaise. It was faster and more comfortable than a stage coach, although the fare was far more expensive. With fresh horses hired from inns along the route, a post-chaise could travel up to 80 km (50 miles) a day. It had no driver, but was controlled by men called "post-boys" or "postilions" who rode the horses.

Post-chaises at a coaching inn, c.1780

c.1760 ROLLER SKATE *Europe*
In 1760, a Belgian musician called Joseph Merlin caused a sensation in London when he entered a fancy-dress ball on roller skates while playing the violin. Unable to stop, he crashed into a £500 mirror and broke it. Merlin's roller skates, made for his own amusement, were not the first. Roller skates were probably invented in Holland at the start of the 18th century. These "ground skates", as they were known, consisted of a rigid, wheeled sole that was attached to a shoe. They were almost impossible to steer around corners.

Dutch engraving of a roller skater, 1790

Steam was produced by heating water in a huge copper boiler.

Steam pipe

Chimney

High-pressure steam from the boiler drove pistons in two bronze cylinders.

The driver turned the tiller to steer the vehicle.

Brake pedal

Model of Cugnot's steam-powered Fardier, 1769

Seat

The two rear wheels and the front driving wheel had broad, iron tyres around their rims.

Log basket

•1769 STEAM-POWERED TRACTOR *France*
In the late 18th century, several people tried to make steam-powered road vehicles. The first to succeed was Nicholas Cugnot, a French army engineer. His three-wheeled tractor was the first "self-propelled" vehicle – that is, able to move under its own power. Designed as a gun carriage, it reached a speed of 5 kph (3 mph) in 1770 pulling a 3-tonne cannon. But Cugnot's hefty tractor, or *Fardier*, was unstable. It capsized in a Paris street, demolishing a wall, and was not used again.

Carrying fork to hold the boiler, which was so heavy it made the vehicle unstable.

The pistons powered a single front driving wheel, via a ratchet mechanism.

The yard was used as a crane.

c.1750 CARGO SHIP *Europe*
By the mid-18th century, cargo ships were transporting people, animals, and goods all over the world. When horses had to be taken abroad they were loaded like other cargo into the ship's hold, where they stood on sand to protect their hooves. Cargo was hoisted onto the ship using one of the yards as a crane. The cargo was carefully loaded to make sure it did not move in stormy seas, and to balance the ship.

Horse lowered into the hold on a harness

Model of an 18th-century cargo ship

c.1770 BARK CANOE *Australia*
Since the earliest days of water travel, people have made boats out of long, wide strips of bark peeled from trees such as birch or eucalyptus. With its ends tied up, the bark naturally takes the shape of a simple but effective canoe. Bark canoes are fast, strong, and light enough to be carried overland on parts of a journey where they cannot be paddled.

Aboriginal eucalyptus canoe, Australia, painted c.1770

1776• SUBMARINE *USA*
The first underwater ship used in war was the *Turtle*, designed by an American named David C. Bushnell. The *Turtle* carried one person, who manoeuvred the craft with two propellers turned by hand. Like all submarines, it was made to sink or rise in the water by pumping water into and out of tanks inside the craft. The *Turtle*'s attempts to attach explosive mines to the British warship HMS *Eagle* off New York were unsuccessful.

Cutaway model of the Turtle, 1776

Horse-drawn canal barge

c.1760 CANAL BARGE *Europe*
As countries in Europe became more industrial, canal traffic increased between important trade centres, and new canals were dug. Loads can be moved more easily on water than on land, so barges drawn by horses became an efficient (if slow) way of transporting heavy cargos such as coal, farm produce, or pottery.

• **1747** A School of Bridges and Highways is set up in France to train engineers in road-building techniques.
• **1748** Jacques Vaucanson, a French engineer, demonstrates a clockwork-powered carriage to the King of France.
1750s Many roads in Britain are now "turnpikes". Tolls are charged on these roads, and the money used to improve them. The first turnpike in the USA will be a new road built in Virginia in 1785.
• **1750** In England, James Heath devises the "bath-chair" as transport for sick or disabled people. It is a small three-wheeled vehicle that is pushed from behind.

• **1756** Stage coach services are in operation in North America by now.
• **1757** John Campbell, an English sailor, invents the sextant, a version of the octant that is more versatile and easier to use. *See* MILESTONES 1731.
• **1759** John Smeaton builds a new lighthouse on the dangerous Eddystone Rocks in the English Channel. It is the first to be built with underwater-setting cement and "dove-tailed" stones, cut to fit into each other like pieces of a jigsaw puzzle.

Sextant

• **1761** Completion of the first part of the Bridgewater Canal in England starts a craze for canal building. This stretch includes the first boat-carrying aqueduct.
• **1768** In his ship *Endeavour*, the English sailor Captain James Cook sets off on the first of three voyages, during which he will explore Australia, New Zealand, Antarctica, and many Pacific islands.
• **1769** In France, Cugnot's ponderous steam tractor becomes the first self-propelled road vehicle.

• **1769** James Watt, a Scot, patents a steam engine that is six times more efficient than Thomas Newcomen's (*see* MILESTONES 1712). Watt will patent his improved "rotative" steam engine in 1782.
• **1776** David C. Bushnell's one-person submarine *Turtle* takes part in the American War of Independence.
• **1779** Abraham Darby III builds the world's first iron bridge over the River Severn at Coalbrookdale in England.
• **1778** Captain Cook arrives in Hawaii and sees surfboards in use there. Hawaiians call surfing "wave-sliding".

1780–1879 Full steam ahead

HOW MUCH SPEED can the human body stand? People asked this question when the first steam trains were built, because they were worried that trains might go so fast that rail passengers would be unable to breathe or would be shaken unconscious by the vibrations. But by the 1850s, train passengers were travelling at previously unheard-of speeds – 80 kph (50 mph) or more – and loving it!

Trains were also more comfortable than other forms of transport, and less likely to grind to a halt in bad weather. Rail travel was cheap, so that people who had never been on a journey before could now afford to go by train. Places that had once seemed far apart suddenly felt much closer, because people and goods could move between them in hours rather than days. In some places, new towns sprang up alongside the tracks.

Even time itself was affected. Before railways came, every town kept its own time, different from the time in towns just a few miles away. But when linked by rail, all clocks in a given area began to run to standard "railway time".

Model of Richard Trevithick's "Catch Me Who Can" locomotive, 1808

The steam age

The invention of the steam engine provided transport with a new energy source. Fuelled by burning coal, or sometimes wood, the first steam engines were huge, lumbering machines that rocked back and forth like see-saws. By the early 1800s, Richard Trevithick in England and Oliver Evans in the USA had developed high-pressure engines that were small enough to mount on wheels, yet

Coal-carrying tender

Steam whistle

Driver's cab

German horse-drawn wagonway, late 18th century

THE RAILWAY AGE
Before the invention of the steam engine, heavy loads were carried in wagons running on wooden planks, pulled either by horses or people. But steam locomotives proved far more powerful, and with smoother, stronger rails, they were also much faster. After the first steam locomotives of the early 1800s, railways expanded rapidly, with a dramatic impact on daily life in many countries.

THE CHANGING WORLD: 1780–1879

Sketch of Cayley's glider, 1853

SCIENCE AND TRANSPORT
By 1840, the word "scientist" had been devised to describe people who carry out experiments to discover how nature works. Scientific discoveries soon played an important role in the development of transport. The work of Michael Faraday in England and Joseph Henry in the USA, for example, showed how electricity could be used to power motors, which would one day drive trams and trains. And as early as 1809, English experimenter Sir George Cayley outlined the basic rules that enable machines to fly.

EXPANDING CITIES
During the 19th century, cities expanded rapidly as people moved from farm work to factory jobs. The populations of a number of cities grew to more than 1 million. Many people could no longer live near enough to the centre to be able to walk to work, so new transport systems were developed. Horse-drawn buses and trams came first, and were soon joined by electric trams, and railways running underground or overhead.

New York elevated railway, late 19th century

Model of the slave ship *Brookes*, used by anti-slavery campaigners, c.1790

NEW INVENTIONS
The 19th century was a time of great technological change. Some inventors published their plans for machines that might speed up travel or save labour in the factory or the home. Others went straight ahead and turned their ideas into reality, building steam vehicles or outlandish bicycles, for example, and trying them out in public. Many inventions were instant failures – but not all. The elevator, or lift, and its later rival the escalator soon caught on, and are still "people-movers" today.

Otis elevator

RELUCTANT TRAVELLERS
Not everyone who travelled did so willingly. From Britain, convicted criminals were exiled to Australia, where they faced harsh conditions. And, over the course of 300 years, European "traders" forcibly shipped 10 million innocent Africans to the West Indies and countries in North and South America, where they were sold as slaves. Slave ships carried several hundred people chained below deck in appalling conditions. Many died during the long journey.

powerful enough to drive the wheels themselves. These "locomotives" were set to work on railways, and they soon put horse-drawn stage coaches out of business. Some inventors developed steam road carriages, but they were heavy vehicles, difficult to manoeuvre on uneven roads. After several accidents, they became unpopular. On water, steam engines were used first to turn the paddle wheels and then the propellers of ships. But steam was slow to overtake wind power. Magnificent sailing ships continued to make their stately way across the world's oceans throughout the 19th century.

A new dimension

Ballooning caused as much sensation as the early railways. "Aeronauts" rose above admiring crowds in the 1780s, lifted first by hot air, then by hydrogen gas. Ballooning was not yet a serious form of transport, as balloonists were at the mercy of the wind and had little control over where they landed. A number of inventors experimented with gliders and other types of aircraft. But proper powered flight could not be achieved with steam engines. By 1880, a more compact engine, the internal combustion engine, had been developed. It would have a huge effect on transport in the next century.

Model of an American coal-burning locomotive of 1875

Steam dome

Warning bell

The "cowcatcher" pushes aside roaming animals such as cattle and buffalo.

THE TECHNOLOGY OF TRANSPORT

FLOATING ON AIR

Like fishes in water, balloons float in air because their weight exactly balances the weight of the material they displace. Air expands when it is heated, so a balloonful of hot air is lighter than the same volume of cold air. If the combined weight of the balloon, its passengers and ballast, and the hot air inside it equals the weight of cold air that would fill the same space, the balloon will float. Heat the air a little more, or throw out some ballast, and the balloon will rise. Allow the air inside the balloon to cool, and it will gradually sink to the ground.

The Montgolfier brothers' hot-air balloon *Flesselles*, 1784

HIGH-PRESSURE STEAM

Energy had been locked away in coal for millions of years before the steam engine came along to convert it into something more useful – the ability to drive machines. When coal or other fuel is burned in the boiler of a steam engine, the heat released changes water into steam. Because the steam in the boiler is under high pressure, it carries a lot of energy. When the steam flows into a cylinder, its pressure pushes back a piston – rather like a bicycle pump working in reverse. The back-and-forth movement of the piston can be harnessed, via a crank, to turn the wheels that drive a ship's propeller, move a locomotive, or run machines in a factory.

Main crank

Cross-section of a paddle-steamer, c.1840

Paddle wheel

Piston rod

Steam pipe

ENGINEERING FEATS

The work of civil engineers was vital to the spread of railways, roads, and canals. Using new construction techniques and materials, engineers were able to plan routes across even the most difficult terrain. They built stronger bridges, longer tunnels, and more durable roads. Successful engineers became popular heroes. But they also had to be good at persuading people to finance their daring schemes. Engineering failures, such as the collapse of a bridge, were not uncommon – and neither were financial failures.

A train emerges from a railway tunnel in England, late 19th century

American settlers in a "prairie schooner" wagon, 1859

MASS MIGRATION

At a time when most people had never travelled more than a few miles from home, 10 million Europeans crossed the Atlantic to settle in North America. Another 10 million moved south to Australia, South America, and other countries. They travelled cheaply but uncomfortably by ship, driven out by overcrowding and poverty in Europe, and lured by the chance to make a new start. Pioneer settlers in the USA still faced long overland journeys before they reached their destinations.

IRON AND STEEL

A new way of making iron – using coke in the furnace instead of charcoal – was crucial to the industrialization of Europe and North America. Iron was used to make the cylinders of early steam engines, and the first metal rails on wagonways. Later, steel – a tough metal made by adding carbon and other materials to iron – became available. Steel is used to make ships, tools, railway tracks, and girders.

The Iron Bridge at Coalbrookdale, England, c.1790

Child's tricycle, 19th century

PLEASURE TRAVEL

Transport developments in the 19th century gave many people the opportunity to travel for fun. Railway companies organized outings to the seaside, called "excursions", and weekend river trips by paddle boat were enjoyed by millions. For the wealthier, the new railways made foreign travel a pleasure rather than an ordeal. But in the days before the motor car, it was cycling that became the really affordable leisure activity. It was an ideal way to see the countryside and keep fit at the same time.

1780

1790

AIR

•1783
HOT-AIR BALLOON *France*
The French brothers Étienne and Joseph Montgolfier began a new era in transport on 21 November, 1783, when their vast hot-air balloon became the first to fly freely with people on board. With its two passengers, Pilâtre de Rozier and the Marquis d'Arlandes, the paper-and-cotton balloon made a safe landing after a 25-minute flight that took them 9 km (5.5 miles) across Paris.

Model of the Montgolfier brothers' balloon, 1783

Garnerin's parachute descent, 1797

•1797
PARACHUTE DESCENT *France*
On 22 October, 1797, the Frenchman André-Jacques Garnerin made the first parachute descent from an aircraft. He bravely cut himself loose from a hydrogen balloon at a height of 700 m (2,300 ft) over Paris. His canvas parachute, 12 m (40 ft) across, opened perfectly, but swung violently from side to side as it came down. Garnerin was air-sick, but otherwise unharmed. Later parachutes had a hole in the centre to let the air inside escape and stop them from swinging.

LAND

Bath mail coach, 1784

1784•
MAIL COACH *England*
Mail services were greatly improved when letters began to be carried in special coaches, rather than on horseback. Mail coaches were faster than stage coaches and, with an armed guard alongside the driver, they were less likely to be robbed.

c.1790 STAGE COACH *Europe*
Gaudily painted stage coaches ran regular services between towns and cities, but the passengers often got an uncomfortable ride as they rattled over bumpy roads. More people rode on the outside of a coach than inside, making it liable to overturn. "Outsiders" had fresh air and a fine view, but were more likely to be hurt in the frequent accidents, and they occasionally froze to death in wintry weather.

Boarding a stage coach

Model of Murdock's tricycle

•1784 STEAM TRICYCLE *England*
A steam-powered three-wheeler, less than 0.5 m (1.6 ft) high, was built by William Murdock, one of James Watt's assistants. It hissed its way successfully through the streets of Redruth, in Cornwall, England. Murdock planned a full-size version, powerful enough to pull a carriage, but it was never built.

The small burner boiled water to produce steam.

The outrigger is connected to the hull by a platform. This canoe even has a hut built on the platform.

Under sail, the wooden outrigger skims the water's surface.

WATER

•1786
STEAMBOAT *USA*
The American inventor John Fitch pioneered the use of steam power to drive river boats. One of his early experimental boats had 12 vertical oars that were moved back and forth by the steam engine. A later version provided a passenger service between Pennsylvania and New Jersey on the Delaware River, but it went out of business after a few months. Fitch also experimented with propeller-driven craft.

Fitch's steamboat on the Delaware River, 1786

Model of "Tepuke" canoe, Solomon Islands

The crew transfer their weight to the leeward side of the platform to stop the float being submerged.

c.1790 OUTRIGGER *Pacific islands*
Pacific island peoples made ocean journeys in dug-outs fitted with sails. Dug-outs are unstable under sail, so a float called an "outrigger" was often added to the hull. An outrigger is kept facing the wind ("windward"), to balance the pressure of the wind on the sail. If it were away from the wind ("leeward"), the wind would force it underwater, tearing it from the hull.

Outrigger canoes have a symmetrical hull, with no fixed bow or stern. To change direction, the sail is reset at the other end of the canoe.

MILESTONES

•**1780s** Copper plates are fitted to the bottoms of ships' hulls to protect them from worms, barnacles, and weeds that slow them down.
•**1783** On 21 November, the Montgolfier brothers' hot-air balloon carries the first two people ever to fly. On 1 December, two more Frenchmen, Professor Charles and his mechanic Robert, make the first flight in a hydrogen balloon. Balloon ascents will follow in Italy and Britain in 1784; Holland, Belgium, and Germany in 1785; and the USA in 1793.
•**1783** In France, Sebastien Lenormand makes parachute descents from a tree and a tower.
•**1783** The Marquis Jouffroy d'Abbans builds a successful steam paddle boat in France.

•**1784** In England, a regular mail coach service (probably the world's first) starts from London to Bath. Mail coaches are exempt from road tolls.

Fan commemorating Charles' first balloon flight, 1783

•**1790s** Trade between Europe and the Far East is now carried by ships of 1,200 tonnes or more, called "East Indiamen". One East Indiaman, the *Essex*, can set as many as 63 separate sails.
•**1792** In France, the emperor Napoleon's surgeon devises a horse-drawn ambulance to carry wounded soldiers. It has springs to smooth the ride over bumpy ground.
•**1794** A ball bearing is patented by Philip Vaughan in England. Ball bearings enable wheels to turn more easily, and will become important in the development of the bicycle and other machines.

•**1796** Wooden warships *Constitution* and *President* are launched in the USA, and are the largest and best of their type.
•**1797** Richard Trevithick in England and Oliver Evans in the USA start to develop high-pressure steam engines, which will eventually make steam railways possible.
•**1797** In Paris, André-Jacques Garnerin makes the first free parachute descent from a balloon.
•**1799** The first design for an aeroplane is sketched by English nobleman Sir George Cayley. It has a fixed wing, a separate tail, a rudder for side-to-side control, and elevators for up-and-down control.

1800

1810

Degen's ornithopter, 1809

•1809•
ORNITHOPTER *Austria*
Over the centuries, many people have tried to copy the way birds fly, but all without success. Some attached feathers to their bodies and attempted to glide from the tops of towers. Most were injured as they fell to the ground. Others ran along, flapping their "wings" as they tried to get airborne. Mechanical flapping-machines called "ornithopters" were also used. Jacob Degen, a Swiss inventor living in Vienna, managed to get his ornithopter off the ground – but only because it was attached to a hydrogen balloon.

So much smoke and noise came from the chimney that people complained.

Piston rod

Steam produced in the boiler moved the pistons, which, in turn, powered the driving wheels.

The sail, made of matting, is a specialized type of lateen.

Furnace

Coal wagon

Madame Blanchard falls to her death

•1819
BALLOON ACCIDENT
France
Before a huge crowd in Paris, Marie-Madeleine Blanchard, the first professional woman balloonist, gave a firework display from a hydrogen balloon in 1819. All was going well as she ascended in a "golden rain" of sparks and fire. But hydrogen from the balloon suddenly caught fire, and Madame Blanchard was killed as the balloon plunged to the ground.

•1805
STEAM VEHICLE *USA*
Oliver Evans, an American engineer, mounted a high-pressure steam engine in a flat-bottomed boat for use as a dredger in the Schuylkill River. To reach the river, he fitted the boat with wheels and used the steam engine to drive it 2 km (1.2 miles) along the streets of Philadelphia. This strange amphibious craft was the first self-propelled vehicle in the United States.

The distinctive shape of the "crab-claw" or "half-moon" sail helps to keep the sail flat in strong winds.

Puffing Billy, 1813

•1817 RUNNING
MACHINE *Germany*
One of the earliest ancestors of the bicycle was the "running machine", devised by a German Baron named Karl von Drais. It had no brakes or pedals. Riders sat on the saddle, leaned forward on a padded support, and propelled themselves forward with huge strides of their legs. In Britain, it was called the "hobby horse". Riders could reach speeds of up to 15 kph (9.5 mph).

Hedley's locomotives and wagons had flanged wheels.

•1813
PUFFING BILLY *England*
Some railway builders thought the new steam locomotives would not grip the iron track well enough to haul long, heavy trains. But William Hedley, the engineer of a horse-drawn railway in the north of England, proved them wrong. He converted his railway to steam, building locomotives that could haul 50-tonne trains of coal wagons.

Hobby horse, c.1820

Oliver Evans' steam vehicle 1805

The ship is called a lugger because it is rigged with angled lugsails.

The paddle wheels were detached and laid on the deck when the ship was under sail.

•1800 LUGGER *Europe*
Many varieties of small vessel have been used for sailing close to the shore, for example by fishermen or to carry loads from port to port around the coast. The special feature of the type known as a "lugger" was its trapezoidal sails set almost fore-and-aft along the line of the boat. Luggers were particularly popular with smugglers, who needed to bring their contraband ashore at places where there was no proper harbour.

1819•
SAVANNAH *USA*
The *Savannah* combined sail and steam power. Its masts could be fully rigged, but it also had paddle wheels, powered by a small steam engine, to keep it moving when the wind was not right for sailing. In 1819, *Savannah* became the first "steamer" to cross the Atlantic, but it relied on the sails alone for most of the journey.

Model of *Savannah*, 1819

Model of a French lugger, c.1800

•**1800s** The "Coaching Age" approaches its height in Europe. Many new types of private coach are introduced, and the roads, which are being improved, are very busy with horse-drawn traffic.
•**1801** Richard Trevithick runs a steam road carriage at 13 kph (8 mph) in Cornwall, England. It eventually catches fire after he lets the engine boil dry.
•**1803** The world's first public railway opens near London, England. Its horse-drawn trains carry goods only. The first railway for fare-paying passengers, also horse-drawn, opens at Oystermouth in South Wales a few years later.

•**1803** In England, Richard Trevithick builds the first steam railway locomotive.
•**1804** Coach travel improves with the invention of elliptical metal suspension springs by Obadiah Elliot in England. They will later be used on motor cars.
•**1806** Rockets are used for the first time in European warfare. The British fire 2,000 of them against the French in 30 minutes.
•**1807** The first reliable steamboat, Robert Fulton's *Clermont*, operates on the Hudson River, USA.

Military rockets, 1806

•**1812** Commercial steamboats begin to run on the Mississippi River in the USA.
•**1813** William Hedley shows that locomotives with metal wheels can pull trains on metal rails without slipping. The wheels have a lip, or flange, that fits inside the flat rail to guide the train.
•**1816–20** John McAdam, a Scot, develops an improved method of surfacing roads. He and his sons will build 3,200 km (2,000 miles) of roads in Britain. His method will be widely used elsewhere.

•**1817** In Germany, Baron von Drais devises his "Draisine" running machine.
•**1818** The US government builds a road called the "National Pike" linking towns in Maryland and West Virginia – possibly the first major US highway.
•**1818** French-born Marc Isambard Brunel invents a tunnel-boring machine.
•**1819** The Danish scientist Hans Christian Oersted discovers the link between magnetism and electricity. In 1821, Englishman Michael Faraday will use this discovery to make the first electric motor, although it will have no real practical use. See **MILESTONES 1831**.

1820   1825

| 1820 | 1821 | 1822 | 1823 | 1824 | 1825 | 1826 | 1827 | 1828 | 1829 |

AIR

Cartoon by George Cruikshank, showing balloon "taxis", 1825

1825·
BALLOON MANIA *Europe*
The early balloons caused great excitement. Some ascents were made by scientists who wanted to study the atmosphere, but many more were made by professional balloonists who were also great entertainers. They travelled to fêtes and other celebrations and performed in front of large crowds. Some people placed bets on how far a balloon would fly before it came down. Even cartoonists joined in the fun, using their imagination to conjure up bizarre scenes showing how balloons might be used in the future.

The tall chimneys meant that there could be no low bridges on the first railway lines.

Tall, narrow chimneys made the early locomotives more efficient, because they improved the draught on the fire.

Agenoria was a heavy locomotive, built for hauling coal in the English Midlands.

LAND

Safety valve lets steam escape if pressure in boiler is dangerously high

Hot gases running through copper "fire tubes" in boiler turn water into steam

Pipe taking steam to the pistons

Water barrel

Fuel tender holds coal for locomotive

Wheels are driven by pistons in two separate, angled cylinders

Coal is burned in the "firebox".

Reproduction of Rocket, 1829

Flanged wheels

Agenoria, 1829

1829·
ROCKET *England*
In 1829, a contest – the Rainhill trials – was held to find the best locomotive to run on the Liverpool to Manchester railway in northwest England. *Novelty* and *Sans Pareil* were easily beaten by *Rocket*, built largely by the engineer Robert Stephenson. In the same year, the English-built *Stourbridge Lion* became the first locomotive to run on rails in the USA. Almost identical to *Agenoria*, shown above, *Stourbridge Lion* proved too heavy for American tracks.

WATER

c.1820 MAORI CANOE *New Zealand*
The Maori people arrived in New Zealand about 1,000 years ago, probably travelling by canoe from other Pacific islands. Their war canoes, used until the late 19th century, were up to 20 m (65 ft) long and decorated with elaborate carvings. Each canoe was made from the hollowed-out trunk of a single pine tree as much as 3 m (10 ft) across, making it strong and durable. It could take several years to build such a canoe. War canoes were paddled by as many as 100 warriors. Occasionally, a sail shaped like an inverted triangle was positioned at the front, to give greater speed.
See **DUG-OUTS C.7000 BC**.

Model of Dutch canal boat, c.1825

The main sail is attached to the mast by a curved beam called a "gaff".

The boat is rigged fore-and-aft.

Many canoes had an ornate raised sternpost.

Model of Maori war canoe, c.1820

c.1825 CANAL BOAT *Holland*
Small, flat-bottomed sailing boats plied the canals of the Low Countries in the 19th century. With fore-and-aft sails (*see* **LATEEN-RIGGED CRAFT 200 BC**), they were liable to drift sideways in the wind. To counter this, a flat board called a "leeboard" was lowered into the water on one side of the boat. As an alternative, many sailing boats have a centreboard, which is lowered through a slit in the centre of the hull.

Leeboard

Bailer for shovelling water out of the boat

Each figure is surrounded by a waterproof covering with a drawstring to keep water out.

Spears, harpoons, and clubs for hunting

Wooden oar

MILESTONES

1820–1829

•**1820s** Experimental steam-powered vehicles appear on the roads in several countries.
•**1820** Engineer Thomas Telford has now constructed 1,500 km (930 miles) of new roads in Britain. This includes the building of 1,117 bridges.
•**1821** In England, Charles Green makes the first ascent in a balloon filled with coal gas.
•**1822** French engineer Marc Seguin builds an experimental "suspension" bridge that hangs from wire cables.

•**1825** The Stockton to Darlington railway opens in England. Trains run on 3-m (10-ft) iron rails, and cross the first iron railway bridge.
•**1825** In France, Marc Seguin invents the fire-tube boiler to make steam locomotives more efficient.
•**1825** The 580-km (360-mile) Erie Canal opens in the USA. It enables boats to travel from the Atlantic Ocean to the Great Lakes.

The Erie Canal

•**1826** In Nantes, France, a Monsieur Baudry runs a regular passenger service in a horse-drawn vehicle, which he calls an "omnibus".
•**1827** In France, Onésiphore Pecqueur invents "differential" gearing, which allows wheels on one side of a vehicle to turn faster than those on the other side when turning corners. It will later be used for motor cars.

•**1828** Tourism comes a step nearer when Karl Baedeker publishes a guide book in Germany. It is called *The Rhine from Mainz to Cologne*.
•**1829** A competition at Rainhill in England to find the best steam locomotive is won by Robert Stephenson's *Rocket*.
•**1829** *Stourbridge Lion*, a British-built locomotive, is the first to run in the USA, but is not a success.

1830

1835

Sansons' dirigible, 1839

Royal Vauxhall's long-distance flight, 1836

•1839• DIRIGIBLE BALLOON
France
Ballooning could not be a serious form of transport until it was possible to build "airships" or "dirigibles" – balloons that could be steered as they flew. The first step was to change the balloon's shape, making a long balloon that cut more easily through the air. The second step was to find a means of propulsion. Suggestions included propellers turned by the passengers and jets of hot air blowing out at the back. The Sansons, a French father and son team, planned a dirigible driven by flapping wings and paddle wheels.

•1836• LONG-DISTANCE BALLOON *England*
The English aeronaut Charles Green's greatest balloon was the *Royal Vauxhall*. Made from 1,850 m (6,070 ft) of Italian silk and standing 25 m (80 ft) high, it was filled with coal gas. On 7 November, 1836, Green and two companions took off from London in the *Royal Vauxhall*. Their record-breaking flight ended the next morning 770 km (480 miles) away, near Weilburg in the Duchy of Nassau (now part of Germany).

•1835• PHAETON *Europe/USA*
By the early 19th century, there was a vast array of different private carriages from which to choose, with styles to suit every occasion. With its high seat and open top, the elegant four-wheeled phaeton was the carriage for people who wanted to look fashionable about town. First used in France, the phaeton also became popular in England and the USA.

Phaeton, c.1835

•1838• MULE CART *India*
Small carts have changed very little in 3,000 years. The mule cart below is from rural India, where it was used both for personal transport and for carrying farm produce to market. A mule is the offspring of a female horse and a male donkey. Hardy and sure-footed, mules can withstand both heat and cold, and can walk up to 80 km (50 miles) in a day.

Indian mule cart, 1838

Best Friend of Charleston

•1830 BEST FRIEND OF CHARLESTON *USA*
The first American-built locomotives were usually lighter than English ones, and some had the boiler, in which water is changed to steam, mounted vertically instead of horizontally. *Best Friend of Charleston* pulled trains on the South Carolina Railroad until a mechanic one day held down the safety valve, causing the boiler to explode violently. It was later rebuilt and its name changed to *Phoenix*.

Model kayak

c.1830 KAYAK *Alaska*
When European traders and explorers visited the Arctic, they saw Inuit people hunting sea otters from skin-covered canoes called "kayaks". These boats had probably changed very little in hundreds of years. To keep out water, the kayak's wooden frame was completely covered with seal skin, leaving only small openings for people to sit in. The three-person kayak may have been developed by Russian traders from smaller Inuit kayaks. Skin-covered kayaks are still used today in Greenland.

Carved figurehead at front of canoe

British East Indiaman, 1836

Model of *Sirius*, 1838

•1838 SIRIUS *Ireland*
Sirius was the first ship to cross the Atlantic entirely under its own steam. But it nearly ran out of coal, and only completed the journey by burning its cabin furniture, spare yards, and one mast in order to keep the steam up in its boiler. *Sirius* left Cork, Ireland, on 4 April, reaching New York, USA, after 18 days and 10 hours at sea. The *Great Western*, a more powerful steamship, arrived 4 hours later, having crossed from Bristol, England, in just 15 days. The *Great Western* was specially designed for transatlantic voyages, so it still had plenty of coal left when it reached New York. See SAVANNAH 1819.

•1836• EAST INDIAMAN *Europe*
For more than 200 years, trade between Europe and Asia was dominated by "East India companies" based in Europe. Their magnificent sailing ships were called "East Indiamen". These armed trading ships carried gold and silver on the outward journey, and brought back jewellery, spices, tea, porcelain, and furniture to Europe.

•**1830** The Liverpool to Manchester line in England is the first to provide a regular time-tabled service with steam-powered passenger and freight trains. The trains soon replace the local stage coach service, because they are cheaper and quicker.
•**1830** *Best Friend of Charleston* is the first successful steam locomotive to be built in the USA. In 1831, it reaches 40 kph (25 mph) on its first run in Carolina.
•**1830** The first railway tunnel is built, on England's Canterbury to Whitstable line.
•**1830** America's first successful balloonist, Charles Durant, makes his maiden flight from New York.

•**1831** The engineer Marc Seguin's steam locomotives go into service in France. In the next few years, steam railways start up in Austria, Belgium, Canada, Holland, Italy, Russia, Spain, Sweden, and Switzerland.
•**1831** American Joseph Henry makes a practical electric motor, which uses direct current from a battery.
•**1832** Horse-drawn tram services start in New York, USA, and in France.

Early screw propeller

•**1836** Screw propellers for ships are successfully tested in England by Francis Pettit Smith and by John Ericsson, a Swedish-American.
•**1837** Inventors in Britain and America develop the electric telegraph, a form of instant communication that will be widely used by railways.
•**1838** Two ships – *Sirius* and *Great Western* – cross the Atlantic under steam power alone. Regular transatlantic passenger services soon follow.

Brunel's *Great Western*, 1837

•**1839** A 25-m (80-ft) cast-iron bridge across Dunlap's Creek in Pennsylvania is the first all-metal bridge in the USA.
•**1839** Kirkpatrick Macmillan, a Scottish blacksmith, builds a pedal-powered bicycle, but the idea does not catch on. See MILESTONES 1885.
•**1839** A battery-powered electric paddle boat is built in Russia.

1840   1845

| 1840 | 1841 | 1842 | 1843 | 1844 | | 1846 | 1847 | 1848 | 1849 |

AIR

•1843 AERIAL STEAM CARRIAGE Britain

Despite all the excitement over balloons, a few pioneers were interested in developing "heavier-than-air" flying machines, later called aeroplanes. William Henson showed what the future might hold when he proposed a huge "Aerial Steam Carriage", designed to carry passengers from Europe to China. But with a heavy steam engine to drive its propellers, such a machine could never have got off the ground.

Henson's Aerial Steam Carriage, 1843

Propeller fitted here

Stringfellow's monoplane, 1848

Housing for steam engine

Curved wing of wood and canvas

Separate tail

•1848 STEAM-POWERED MONOPLANE Britain

It has been claimed that the first powered machine ever to fly was a 3-m (10-ft) wide steam-powered model built by John Stringfellow. This was a single-winged machine, or "monoplane", with two propellers. It showed many of the important features of future aircraft. Launched from an overhead wire, the model lacked stability, and soon fell to the ground.

Chimney

Steam dome

Bogie

LAND

c.1840 PRAIRIE SCHOONER USA

Families moving to settle in the American West made the journey in rugged, canvas-covered wagons pulled by teams of mules or oxen. From a distance, the white-topped wagons looked like sailing ships as they crossed the wide grasslands (prairies), so they were called "prairie schooners". Convoys of 100 or more wagons travelled about 30 km (20 miles) a day on a trek that could take up to five months.

Prairie schooner, c.1840

Fuel tender

Model Norris locomotive, 1843

Driving wheel

•1843 LOCOMOTIVE USA

As railways expanded rapidly, new companies were formed to supply them with locomotives. Those built by William Norris' company in Philadelphia, USA, had their main driving wheels at the back. The front rested on a four-wheeled "bogie" that could swivel as the locomotive negotiated sharp bends.

London "knife-board" omnibus, 1847

•1847 OMNIBUS England

Early London omnibuses were small, because they were taxed according to the number of passengers they could carry. When the tax was abolished, buses with seats on the roof were introduced to carry more people. These double-deckers were called "knife-boards", because the back-to-back seats resembled a board used for cleaning knives. Passengers climbed up iron rungs to reach the top deck.

WATER

c.1840 MERCHANT BRIG Europe

Magnificent wooden sailing ships continued to carry their cargoes across the world's oceans throughout the 19th century, even though steamships – and ships built of iron or steel – were beginning to appear. To keep moving when the wind was very light, the crew of a two-masted "brig" might hoist more than twenty separate square or triangular sails. In strong winds most sails would be "furled", or rolled up, leaving only one or two to catch the wind.

Model of a merchant brig, c.1840

Bowsprit

Extra sails were hung from small yards, and booms added to the main yards.

•1845 SAMPAN China

The flat-bottomed wooden craft called "sampans" have been widely used in China and other Eastern countries for many years. On rivers, sampans were usually rowed, but in coastal waters, one or two masts were added to carry sails. Some had a raised deck at the stern while others – like this model – carried a simple shelter "amidships" (in the middle of the boat). Sampans are still used for fishing and for carrying goods, and in overcrowded areas people even make their homes in them.

The boatman propels the sampan with a single oar.

The roofing is made of matting.

Decorated Chinese model sampan

MILESTONES

| 1840–1844 | | 1845–1849 | |

•**1840s** Long, low sailing ships called "clippers" start to be used for bringing tea to Europe and America from China.

•**1840s** Railway signals of the semaphore (moving arm) type begin to replace flags and banners for communicating with the drivers of moving trains.

•**1840s** Large numbers of pioneers begin to migrate to the American West. Each spring, convoys of "prairie schooners" set off on the arduous trek from Independence, Missouri.

•**1841** In England, Thomas Cook runs his first excursion, a special train from Leicester to Loughborough. The world tourist trade will grow from this small beginning.

•**1841** Rail passengers can now travel 250 km (150 miles) in less than 7 hours – three times more quickly than travelling by stage coach.

•**1842** In France, 53 people die in the world's first major train crash, when a locomotive pulling an express train breaks one of its axles.

•**1844** An English sailor named Peter Halket makes the world's first inflatable boat out of canvas and rubber.

•**1845** R.W. Thompson patents his "aerial tyres" in England. These air-filled, or pneumatic, tyres give a comfortable ride and are used on some horse-drawn carriages.

•**1845** Brunel's iron ship *Great Britain* becomes the first propeller-driven liner to cross the Atlantic Ocean.

•**1847** In the USA, an experimental electric car is built by Moses G. Farmer.

Launch of the *Great Britain*, 1845

•**1848** John Stringfellow's steam-powered model aeroplane is launched in Britain, and almost flies.

•**1848** The first railway in South America opens, linking Georgetown and Plaisance in Guyana.

•**1849** A suspension bridge built across the Ohio River in America is the first to be more than 300 m (1,000 ft) long. It is supported by iron wires, but collapses in a gale a few years later.

•**1849** The Austrians send 200 pilotless hot-air balloons towards Venice. The balloons carry bombs, but the "air raid" fails because the wind changes direction.

1850

Poitevin's equestrian ascent, 1850

•1850
HORSEBACK BALLOON *France*

As the public lost interest in ordinary balloon flights, some balloonists tried more risky feats. One stunt was to fly aloft with animals – or even riding on their backs. The French balloonist Poitevin took off on his pony *Blanche* from the Paris Hippodrome in 1850. There were protests against the cruelty of such flights. In fact, on a visit to England in 1852, the courts banned Poitevin's wife from making an ascent on a bull!

•1850 HORSE-POWERED
LOCOMOTIVE *Germany*

Steam locomotives were expensive to buy and run, so on small railway lines horses continued to pull trains. Enthusiastic inventors tried to find alternatives to the steam locomotive. Some devised "atmospheric" railways, for example, using air pressure to push the trains along. Others built curious locomotives that were powered by horses walking on a moving belt. But nothing could compete with the increasing speed and power of steam locomotives.

Horse-powered locomotive, 1850

•1852
STEAM AIRSHIP *France*

In 1852, a French engineer named Henri Giffard designed a dirigible powered by a 2.25 kW (3 hp) steam engine, which turned a propeller 3.4 m (11 ft) in diameter. On 24 September, 1852, Giffard, dressed in top hat and frock-coat, piloted his airship on a 27-km (17-mile) journey from the centre of Paris. Although Giffard's airship only travelled at 10 kph (6 mph), it was the first successful powered flight ever made.

Steering rudder

Landing ropes to tie down airship

Model of Giffard's airship, 1852

Elephant with howdah, 1852

•1852 ELEPHANT *India*

From a covered seat, or "howdah", fixed to an elephant's back, Indian royalty had a superb all-round view when they went hunting. As the elephant crossed rugged country and even rivers, the hunters sat above in comfort and safety. *See* ARMOURED ELEPHANT c.1600.

•1854
STEAM CARRIAGE *Italy*

Engineers in several countries dreamed of steam vehicles that would rival horse-drawn stage coaches. A number of carriages were made, including one built in Turin, Italy, by Virgilio Bordino, an Italian army engineer. Bordino's vehicle achieved 8 kph (5 mph) on a level road. It used the body of a "landau", a popular horse-drawn carriage of the time.

Chimney *Landau body* *Steering tiller*

Boiler

Brake lever

Steam engine

Bordino's steam carriage, 1854

Towing bar

Sail of matted palm leaves

Model of an Indonesian boat used to hunt sperm whales

Whaling scene, 1855

Harpoon

Paddle

Eye for the boat to see with

•1855
WHALING SHIPS

For hundreds of years, local sailors throughout the world hunted whales for meat. This Indonesian boat was used to hunt whales three times its own size. In the 19th century, the demand for whale products in Europe and North America was so great that thousands of whales were slaughtered every year. Whales were killed by harpoons thrown from rowing boats, and then towed back to a larger ship, a "whaler", where oil and other products were extracted.

•1858
GREAT EASTERN *Britain*

Designed by the British engineer Isambard Brunel, *Great Eastern* had many innovations. More than 200 m (650 ft) long, its hull was made of two layers of iron plates. It had five masts to carry sails, but was also powered by steam, with a four-bladed propeller as well as two paddle wheels. *Great Eastern* was a technical success and made 11 transatlantic trips, but it could not attract enough passengers to run at a profit.

Model of *Great Eastern*, 1858

•**1850s** Railway networks expand rapidly. There are now 14,500 km (9,000 miles) of track in the USA, and 9,800 km (6,100 miles) in Britain. Railways begin to take over from canals as a means of transporting goods.

•**1850** The development of modern skiing begins when a Norwegian, Sondre Norheim, devises stiffer bindings to attach skis to boots. Loose-bound skis were used for thousands of years in northern Europe and Asia.

•**1852** Henri Giffard's steam-powered airship flies in France.

•**1853** In England, Sir George Cayley builds and tests a person-carrying glider.

•**1853** The first railway in Asia is opened, between Bombay and Thana in India. In the following year, railways will also open in Australia and Brazil.

•**1854** In New York, USA, Eli Otis demonstrates an elevator, or "lift", with a safety device to stop it from plunging to the ground if the cable breaks. As taller buildings are built, Otis elevators will become well known around the world.

Cross-country skiing, Norway

•**1856** Africa gets its first railway line – between Alexandria and Cairo in Egypt.

•**1856** English scientist Henry Bessemer devises a quick and cheap way to make steel in large quantities. Steel will have many uses in transport, especially for the manufacture of cars in the 20th century.

•**1858** Australia's first balloon ascent is made by William Dean in Melbourne.

•**1859** Edwin L. Drake drills the first successful oil well, at Titusville in Pennsylvania, USA. This is the start of a vast oil and gas industry that will supply essential fuel for transport in the 20th century.

•**1859** The French warship *La Gloire* is the first "iron-clad" – a wooden ship with a hull protected by a layer of iron plates.

•**1859** In France, Étienne Lenoir develops the first reliable internal combustion engine, running on coal gas. By the early part of the 20th century, this new type of engine will have revolutionized the world of transport.

1860   1865

AIR

•1863 STEAM HELICOPTER *France*
In the 15th century, the Italian artist and thinker Leonardo da Vinci sketched a simple helicopter to be lifted by a single rotating spiral wing, or "rotor". In the 19th century, Sir George Cayley (*see* **MILESTONES 1853**) and other flight pioneers built a number of successful model helicopters, each of which was lifted by a rotor with several blades. These, and news of Giffard's airship (*see* **STEAM AIRSHIP 1852**), may have inspired the inventor Gabriel de la Landelle to design his fantastic "Steam Airliner". It was never built, and could never have flown.

Gabriel de la Landelle's "Steam Airliner"

•1868 GLIDER *France*
A bold attempt at practical flying was made by a French sea-captain, Jean-Marie le Bris, when he tried out two full-size gliders. Their design was based on the shape of an albatross, a seabird with a huge wingspan that Le Bris had studied on a visit to South America. The gliders were launched from a moving cart and probably had an adjustable tail and wings. Both gliders crashed after a few short trial flights.

Le Bris' glider, 1868

Compartment for driver   *Water tank*   *Pipe taking steam and smoke to water tanks*

Underground railway locomotive, 1866

LAND

•1860 HORSE-DRAWN TRAM *USA/Europe*
Trams running on metal rails embedded in the streets were widely used in American and European cities in the 1860s. Horses could pull many more passengers in a vehicle on smooth rails than in a bus on uneven roads. This gave the passengers a cheaper, faster, and more comfortable ride.

Horse-drawn tram in London, England, c.1860

•1863 UNDERGROUND RAILWAY *England*
As cities grew larger, their streets became choked with horse-drawn traffic. To ease the problem in London, a railway was built beneath the city's streets. Called the "Metropolitan", it was the world's first underground railway. People flocked to use it, even though the smoke from the steam locomotives pulling the trains made it smelly and dirty.

•1869 SLEDGE *Arctic lands*
The lands within the Arctic Circle are covered with snow and ice for much of the year, so sturdy, thick-coated husky dogs were specially bred for pulling sledges. When harnessed to a strong sledge, a team of eight huskies can pull up to 0.5 tonne of cargo. Antarctic explorers used dog sledges when they searched for the South Pole.

Painting of Inuit sledge, 1869

WATER

•1860 IRON WARSHIP *Britain*
War at sea moved into a new era when navies replaced their wooden ships with iron ones, which were less likely to catch fire in battle. HMS *Warrior* was the first warship built entirely of iron. This 40-gun ship could do 15 knots (28 kph/17 mph) under steam, but also carried a full set of sails. To protect it from the guns of enemy ships, *Warrior's* hull was "armoured" with iron plates 11 cm (4.5 in) thick.

Model of HMS *Warrior*, 1860

The American clipper ship *Great Republic*, 1853–72

•1868 CLIPPER SHIPS *USA/Britain*
Clippers were sleek merchant vessels, designed for speed rather than carrying large cargoes. Some clippers averaged 20 knots (37 kph/23 mph) for hours on end. The fastest clipper was the British ship *Thermopylae*, launched in 1868. The American clipper *Great Republic* was the largest wooden sailing ship ever built. Clippers carried cargo and passengers from New York to San Francisco, USA, during California's gold rush of 1849. They raced to bring tea from China in the 1860s and wool from Australia in the 1880s.

MILESTONES

1860–1864

•**1860** HMS *Warrior*, the first iron warship, is launched in Britain.
•**1860** The Pony Express mail service starts in the USA. Letters now reach California from Missouri in only ten days.
•**1861** In France, Ernest Michaux makes a bicycle or "vélocipède" with pedals at the front that riders turn with their feet.
•**1862** French engineer Alphonse Beau de Rochas patents the four-stroke cycle for internal combustion engines. Nikolaus Otto, a German, will build the first one in 1876.

•**1863** The world's first underground railway is opened in London, England.
•**1863** In the USA, James Plimpton designs roller skates that allow the wearer to turn corners.
•**1863** Englishman Thomas Weston patents the friction clutch, a device that connects an engine to its gears and wheels.
•**1864** American George Pullman designs a railway sleeping car with bunk beds. Luxurious "Pullman Cars" will run on many routes in North America and Europe.

1865–1869

The USA is crossed by rail, 1869

•**1865** A British law limits self-propelled road vehicles to 6 kph (4 mph). They must have a man with a red flag walking 55 m (180 ft) ahead.
•**1867** Joseph Monier in France embeds metal rods in wet concrete to make "reinforced concrete".
•**1867** Frenchman L.G. Perreaux creates the first motorcycle when he fits a steam engine to Michaux's vélocipède. *See* **MILESTONES 1861.**
•**1869** The 160-km (100-mile) Suez Canal opens, linking the Mediterranean to the Red Sea.

•**1869** A coast-to-coast railway is completed in the USA when the Central Pacific and Union Pacific Railroads meet near Great Salt Lake.
•**1869** The first cog or "rack-and-pinion" railway opens on the slopes of Mt. Washington, USA. The locomotive has a gear wheel that meshes with a toothed rack between the rails so it does not slip.
•**1869** American engineer George Westinghouse patents a braking system worked by compressed air.

1870

1875

•1872 MUSCLE-POWERED AIRSHIP *France*
Unpowered balloons are at the wind's mercy. In 1870, during the siege of Paris by the Prussian army, more than 60 balloons escaped from the city with 102 passengers and 2,500,000 letters. One, the *Ville d'Orleans*, was blown so far off course that it ended up in Norway. To overcome such problems, the French engineer Dupuy de Lôme designed a hydrogen-filled airship with a hand-driven propeller and a steering rudder. On its first flight, eight men struggled to turn the handles that drove the propeller, but only achieved a speed of 8 kph (5 mph). The balloon was never used again.

**1879•
AIR-POWERED MONOPLANE** *France*
In France, Victor Tatin flew a model aeroplane whose propellers were powered by compressed air stored in the cylinder that made up the aeroplane's body, or "fuselage". With a wingspan of 2 m (6 ft), the model flew around a central pole to which it was tied by a cord. Tatin's model made flights of more than 15 m (50 ft). It attracted much publicity, and gave people an idea of what full-sized aeroplanes might one day look like.

Tatin's model aeroplane, 1879

The model was powered by two propellers.

Model of Dupuy de Lôme's airship, 1872

Brake cord

The brake was worked by winding the brake cord around the handlebars.

Driver's seat *Brake lever* *Petrol engine* *Passenger seat*

Steering column

Brake block

**1871•
ORDINARY** *Britain*
Bicycles called "ordinaries" or "penny farthings" were produced with larger and larger front wheels, so that they went farther for each turn of the pedals. The saddle was placed over the front wheel, which made it difficult to get on and off the machine, but made it easier to pedal.

Foot-rest for use when speeding downhill

Oak frame

Tyres of solid rubber

Brake

Ordinary, 1871

Reconstruction of Marcus' second motor carriage, 1875

Drive belt

The pulley, driven by the belt, turns the rear axle.

•1875 EARLY MOTOR CAR *Austria*
From the 1860s, a new driving force began to challenge the steam engine. This was the internal combustion engine, powered first by gas and later by petrol. Inventors soon used the new engine to propel road vehicles. In Austria, the first experimental "car", built by Siegfried Marcus, was so noisy it was banned by the police. In 1875, his second car proved slightly more successful.

Model of horses pulling a lifeboat to the water's edge, c.1875

Front wheel is 1.2 m (4 ft) in diameter

c.1870 RIVERBOAT *USA*
Steamboats carried passengers and cargoes of cotton and sugar at a leisurely pace up and down the Mississippi River system in the USA. The river is very shallow in places, so they were built as flat-bottomed paddle steamers, with the engines and several decks above the waterline. Passenger riverboats were often luxurious, with fine carpets, chandeliers, and music provided by an orchestra.

**c.1875
LIFEBOAT** *Europe*
Specialized rowing boats for rescuing people at sea were developed in the 19th century. These "lifeboats" were launched from the beach in an emergency. They were broad compared to their length, to make them less likely to capsize. To help them float even when filled with water, they had cork attached around the sides, or air-filled chambers. Some were even "self-righting", so that they returned the right way up after capsizing.

**1879•
REFRIGERATED CARGO SHIP** *Britain*
The invention of refrigeration changed the diet of many people in Europe. With specially designed refrigerated compartments in their holds, ships could bring meat from as far away as America and Australia without it rotting. Because the meat came from vast herds and flocks kept on huge ranches, it was much cheaper than European beef and lamb.

Mississippi paddle steamer, c.1870

***Orient* refrigerated cargo ship, 1879**

•**1870s** Elevated railways go into service in several cities in the USA and Europe. Running above the streets, they are cheaper to build than underground railways.
•**1870s** Nearly 25 million Europeans will buy a one-way ticket across the Atlantic in the next 50 years. They are emigrants seeking a new life in North America. Most travel "steerage", the cheapest class on a boat.
•**1871** The first wind tunnel is built in England. Wind tunnels will be used to test the design of cars and aeroplanes by blowing air past a stationary model.

•**1872** The first railway in Japan opens, linking Tokyo to Yokohama. Japan's first steam riverboat service also starts this year.
•**1872** Thousands of the horses that pull city trams in the USA catch a serious infectious illness, paralysing public transport.
•**1873** Cable tramcars start to run in San Francisco, USA. They are pulled along by gripping a moving cable underneath the track.
•**1874** The first bridge to be made partly of steel is built across the Mississippi River in the USA.

•**1875** Siegfried Marcus tries out a petrol-driven road vehicle in Vienna.
•**1875** Work starts on a tunnel to link England and France under the English Channel. It will be halted by fears that England might be invaded through the tunnel, as will an attempt in 1882.
•**1875** Three Frenchmen reach a record height of 8.6 km (5.3 miles) in the *Zenith* balloon, but two die from cold and asphyxiation.
•**1877** The British navy launches the first steel warship, HMS *Iris*.

The *Zenith* balloon tragedy, 1875

•**1877** A steamship, the *Paraguay*, carries the first cargo of frozen meat from Argentina to Europe.
•**1877** A wrought-iron cantilever bridge across the Kentucky River is the first of its type in the USA. Cantilevers have arms built out from each side and touching in the middle.
•**1878** The world's first oil tanker comes into service on the Caspian Sea between Iran and Russia.
•**1879** The first electric railway is built by the engineer Werner von Siemens, and runs at 6 kph (4 mph) at an exhibition in Berlin, Germany.

1880–1959 Powered flight and the rise of the motor car

Assembly-line production of Model T Fords, 1913

IN 1880, THERE WERE NO CARS in the world. Eighty years later, there were 95 million of them, all powered by petrol-driven internal combustion engines that were faster, lighter, and more powerful than the old steam engines. The internal combustion engine also transformed air and sea travel, and dramatically shaped the course of the 20th century.

Prototypes of the Volkswagen "Beetle", 1936

MOTOR CARS FOR THE MASSES
Early, hand-built cars such as the Rolls-Royce Silver Ghost were hugely expensive. A new way of manufacturing, called "mass production", changed the history of the car. Cars mass-produced on factory assembly lines, such as the Ford Model T and the Volkswagen "Beetle", became cheap enough for ordinary people to afford. Improved roads and specially built intercity motorways made cars a very convenient way to travel.

The petrol engine rings the changes
More than anything else, cars gave their owners the freedom to go where they wanted, when they wanted. With their new mobility, car owners could choose to live far away from where they worked, in areas known as "suburbs" on the outskirts of cities. People who could not afford cars relied mainly on public transport. The early years of the 20th century were a golden age for the railways, and on city streets efficient trams and motor-buses put horse-drawn vehicles out of business. On water, the diesel engine – a type of internal combustion engine – was put to work on smaller vessels, while bigger ships were driven by steam turbines. The age of large sailing ships was virtually at an end.

Hood
Folding windscreen for rear passenger
Windscreen
Rear-view mirror
Wooden-spoked wheel with air-filled "pneumatic" tyre
Rolls-Royce Silver Ghost 40/50, 1909
Toolbox
Spare tyre

THE CHANGING WORLD: 1880–1959

The world's first public electric railway, Lichterfelde, Germany, 1881

ELECTRIC POWER
Electric-powered public transport systems saved the fast-growing cities of the early 20th century from chaos. Taking power from an overhead cable or extra ground rail, electric trains and trams had good acceleration and could stop quickly. Electricity is efficient and pollution-free, but dirty fuels such as coal and oil were still being burned in power stations to generate the electricity.

THE OIL BONANZA
After 1900, petroleum oil began to replace coal as transport's main energy source. Fuels made from this thick, black liquid pack maximum energy into minimum weight and space. Oil, or "liquid gold" as it has been called, is the decomposed remains of marine creatures that lived millions of years ago. It is found in underground reservoirs, and has to be pumped to the surface at oil wells. Oil wells were first established in the USA, and later in Russia, the Middle East, and elsewhere.

The first oil well at Titusville, USA

Wright *Flyer*, 1903

FIRST FLIGHTS
The aeroplane's birth was a quiet one: the 37-m (120-ft) flight by the Wright brothers' *Flyer* in 1903 was hardly noticed by the world at large. The whole of that short "hop" could have taken place inside a modern jumbo jet! The pioneers of powered flight had to work out what size and shape an aeroplane should be, and how to control it. The Wrights used "wing-warping", gentle twisting of the wings, to control the *Flyer*. Later aeroplanes used hinged wing-flaps, called "ailerons", to achieve the same effect.

FLOATING HOTELS
Getting there was more than half the fun in the age of the luxury ocean liner. In the years before World War II, liners grew in size, speed, and comfort, carrying hundreds of wealthy passengers in conditions of the utmost grandeur and elegance. They travelled at a pace that seems relaxed by modern standards – a journey from Europe to America, for example, took four or five days.

The dining room of a luxury liner, c.1910

Opening of a new motorway, or "autobahn", in Germany, 1935

The dawn of the air age

The lightweight internal combustion engine at last made aeroplanes a practical reality. Unlike balloons, the new flying machines could stay aloft even though they were heavier than the air they moved through. Like ballooning a century before, "heavier-than-air" flying was something early enthusiasts did mainly for fun. Only when aeroplanes were used for military purposes during World War I did people begin to take them seriously. Passenger services began to be available in the 1920s, although air travel was still slow and arduous by modern standards. By the 1950s, the first jet airliners were carrying passengers swiftly and comfortably between continents. The pace of development had been so rapid that many people who watched these jets flying overhead could remember a time when there had been no aeroplanes or even cars.

A world divided

The distinctive "Spirit of Ecstasy" mascot was added in 1911.

Despite all the speed and excitement of new forms of transport, the freedom to travel was mostly limited to people in the industrialized countries of North America and Europe. In 1914, for example, the average person in the USA travelled about 2,500 km (1,600 miles) each year, most of it on foot. Fifty years later, they went twice as far each month, mainly by car. In the less developed world, most people were still walking everywhere in 1960.

THE TECHNOLOGY OF TRANSPORT

WINGS – THE SECRET OF POWERED FLIGHT

The top surface of an aircraft wing bulges upwards, while the underside is nearly flat. As an aircraft moves forward, its wing cuts through the air. Some air flows smoothly over the wing, speeding up as it travels over the curved surface; some passes below the wing, with its speed unchanged. Fast-moving air exerts less pressure than slow-moving air, so the downward pressure above the wing is less than the upward pressure below it. The result is an upward force called "lift" that keeps the aircraft aloft. The faster the aircraft goes, the stronger the lift.

Slow-moving air exerts strong upward pressure

Avro triplane IV, 1910

Fast-moving air exerts weaker downward pressure

INTERNAL COMBUSTION

Setting off explosions inside a metal tube seems an unlikely way to power cars, ships, or aircraft – but it works! In most internal combustion engines, a spark ignites a mixture of air and petrol vapour inside a cylinder. The resulting explosion pushes out a piston, whose motion is used to rotate a crank that turns the engine. As the piston falls back, the burned gas is forced out of the cylinder, and a new charge of air and fuel is drawn in for the next explosion. Most engines have at least four cylinders that fire in turn. A diesel engine compresses the air and fuel mixture so much that it explodes of its own accord.

Nikolaus Otto's internal combustion engine of 1888

FARM MACHINERY

The internal combustion engine transformed farming, just as it did many other areas of life. In the 1900s, petrol-powered tractors began to replace draught animals for pulling ploughs and other machinery. By 1950, there were 4 million tractors in the USA and 2 million in the rest of the world. Trucks made it easier for farmers to take produce and animals to market, while self-propelled combine harvesters enabled grain to be harvested more quickly.

Advertisement for "Glasgow" tractor, 1919

RECREATION AND SPORTS

Growing interest in sports and leisure activities promoted improvements in the technology of transport. Water-skiing and surfing, for example, led to the development of new materials from which to make tougher, longer-lasting skis and surfboards. Similarly, the tough demands of long-distance road races helped car makers to know which parts were most likely to break. They could then build more reliable vehicles for general sale.

Water-skiing in the USA, 1920s

THE GOLDEN AGE OF RAILWAYS

For intercity travel, the railways reigned supreme. Fierce competition between rival companies meant that standards of service were higher during the early part of the 20th century than ever before or since. Stations and railway hotels were often grand establishments, and of great architectural merit. By 1960, railways were past their peak in the main industrialized countries, although they were still growing elsewhere.

Grand Central Station, New York, USA, 1913

WAR AND PEACE

During the two World Wars (1914–18 and 1939–45), military forces needed to deliver weapons, troops, and materials rapidly to battle zones. This brought great advances in the technology and design of ships, aeroplanes, and land vehicles. As soon as peace returned, these advances were put to civilian use. For example, work in Germany on liquid-fuelled rockets in the 1940s led directly to American successes in space two decades later.

British Mountain Howitzer gun, World War II

1880

1885

| 1880 | 1881 | 1882 | 1883 | 1884 | 1885 | 1886 | 1889 |

AIR

The hydrogen-filled gas bag was 28 m (92 ft) long.

A rudder in the form of a sail was used to guide the airship.

Model of the Tissandiers' airship, 1883

•1883–84 ELECTRIC-POWERED AIRSHIPS *France*
In their search for a power source to drive an airship, French aeronauts turned to the electric motor. The brothers Gaston and Albert Tissandier built a balloon big enough to lift heavy batteries, a motor, and passengers, but it only crawled through the air at less than 5 kph (3 mph). Charles Renard and Arthur Krebs built an even larger balloon, *La France*. Its batteries and motor weighed nearly 1 tonne, but it managed a speed of 23 kph (14 mph). In a moderate or strong wind, even *La France* could make no headway.

The car was suspended by rigging from a "jacket" around the gas bag.

Renard and Krebs' *La France*, 1884. Powered by an electric motor, it was the first fully controllable airship.

Brake lever

Tank containing water to cool the engine.

Tangent-spoked wire wheel

LAND

c.1880 TRAVOIS *North America*
The North American Indian peoples carried their belongings on a simple vehicle called a travois, made from two long poles and pulled by a dog or horse. The travois has a long history, and may have been used in some parts of the world even earlier than the sledge. *See* **SLEDGE 5000 BC.**

Plains Indians with travois, 1880

1886•
BENZ MOTOR CAR *Germany*
A petrol-driven three-wheeler built by Karl Benz in 1885 can probably be called the world's first true motor car. When Benz showed it in public the following year, the two-seater "Motorwagen" reached a speed of 13 kph (8 mph). The engine was mounted under the passenger seat, and drove the rear wheels by means of a moving belt. Benz set up the first factory to produce three-wheeled and later four-wheeled cars. The car industry grew from these small beginnings.

1885•
DAIMLER MOTORCYCLE *Germany*
A vital step in the development of the motor car came when the German engineer Gottfried Daimler built a petrol engine that turned three times faster than any existing engine. He fixed one of these compact, high-speed engines to a wooden-wheeled bicycle. In 1886, Daimler made a four-wheeled vehicle by attaching an engine to a carriage.

Replica of Daimler motorcycle, 1885

Metal-rimmed wooden wheel

Solid rubber tyres

Benz Motorwagen, 1886

WATER

Servia, the all-steel cargo ship, 1881

1881•
STEEL CARGO LINER *Britain*
The invention of a new and more reliable way of making steel – the Siemens process – meant that ships no longer had to be built of iron. Steel plates were lighter than iron ones, and could be made thinner, but just as strong. *Servia* was the first all-steel cargo ship. It also carried passengers, and was the first ship to have electric lights in its public rooms.

The guns had swivelling mountings so they could fire in several directions.

•1888
STEEL WARSHIP *Japan*
By the late 19th century, navies around the world were strengthening and modernizing their fleets. As Japan emerged as a military and industrial power, its Imperial Navy acquired many new vessels. One of them, the cruiser *Takao*, was the first steel ship built in Japan. Faster and lighter than battleships, cruisers carried guns but were not protected with armour-plating.

Model of Takao, 1888

MILESTONES

1880–1884

•**1880** China's first permanent railway opens.
•**1881** In Germany, the world's first public electric railway opens at Lichterfelde, near Berlin. It is 2.5 km (1.5 miles) long.
•**1882** The 15-km (9-mile) St. Gotthard rail tunnel under the Alps is completed, linking Italy and Switzerland.
•**1882** In Germany, the engineers Gottfried Daimler and Wilhelm Maybach start to develop high-speed petrol engines.

•**1883** The world's longest suspension bridge, the Brooklyn Bridge, opens in New York, USA.
•**1883** The luxurious *Orient Express* rail service carries its first passengers. It runs between Paris, in France, and Constantinople (now Istanbul), in Turkey.
•**1884** British engineer Sir Charles Parsons patents the steam turbine, a form of high-speed steam engine.
•**1884** The first practical airship, *La France*, flies in Paris, powered by a large, electrically driven propeller.

Luxury rail travel in the late 19th century

1885–1889

•**1885** The first specially built oil tanker, the *Glückauf*, is built at Newcastle, England.
•**1885** Karl Benz, a German engineer, builds his petrol-powered "Motorwagen" – the world's first true car.
•**1885** In England, J.K. Starley's "Rover" safety bicycle is the first to use the classic design of two equal-sized wheels, the rear one driven by a chain from the pedals.
•**1886** The first successful tandem bicycles (carrying two people, one behind the other) are built in Britain, and soon become popular.

Dunlop's pneumatic tyres on his son's bicycle

•**1886** The Canadian Pacific Railway's transcontinental route is completed, with a total length of 4,635 km (2,880 miles).
•**1888** Scotsman John B. Dunlop reinvents the air-filled, or "pneumatic", tyre (see **MILESTONES 1845**) for use in his son's bicycle. Pneumatic tyres will soon become standard on all cars and bicycles.
•**1889** After a major rail crash, automatic brakes are made compulsory on British trains.
•**1889** A steam locomotive reaches 143 kph (89 mph) on the Paris–Dijon line in France.

1895

The high wings had a frame like the skeleton of a bat's wing.

•1890
ADER'S ÉOLE *France*
The engineer Clément Ader devised a lightweight but powerful steam engine and fitted it to his bat-winged monoplane *Éole*. With its inventor aboard, *Éole* took off under its own power from a level surface at Armainvilliers, France. It was more of a "hop" than a flight, but *Éole* still managed to skim along close to the ground for about 50 m (165 ft).

— Steering column

Éole's steam engine drove a single propeller with four blades.

Model of Ader's *Éole*, 1891

•1895
GLIDER *Germany*
Launching himself into the wind from suitable high places, Otto Lilienthal made many flights in a range of gliders that he designed and built himself. In his No. 11 glider, he flew a distance of 350 m (1,150 ft), controlling the flight by changing the position of his body, like a modern hang-glider. He died when one of his gliders crashed in 1896. His flights probably inspired the Wright brothers. See **WRIGHT FLYER 1903**.

Lilienthal could control the glider by swinging his legs and changing its centre of gravity.

Cotton wing cover supported by willow ribs

Reconstruction of Lilienthal's No. 11 glider, 1895

Japanese jinrikisha, 1892

1892•
JINRIKISHA *Japan*
A "human horse" ran between the shafts of the jinrikisha, a sort of taxi-cart popular in the cities of Japan and other Asian countries at the end of the 19th century. The runners pulled their "rickshaws", as they were called by European tourists, as far as 48 km (30 miles) in one day. The jinrikisha was banned in many cities, because people felt it was wrong to use people like animals.

•1895
ELECTRIC LOCOMOTIVE *USA*
The first main-line railway to use electric trains was the Baltimore and Ohio in the USA. Six and a half kilometres (4 miles) of track that ran largely in tunnels were converted to electric power, because smoke from steam locomotives was a nuisance. The trains were hauled by electric locomotives, which drew their current from a rigid rail running overhead.

B&O electric locomotive with overhead power rail

•1897 STEAM CAR *USA*
In the early days of motoring, steam cars and petrol cars were rivals. In Massachusetts, USA, the Stanley brothers built a successful steam car that went into commercial production under the name "Locomobile". Although it used 4.5 litres (8 pints) of water every mile and took 30 minutes to get up steam on a cold morning, the Locomobile was so popular that more than 5,000 were sold.

The Stanley Locomobile steam car

Model of Burmese Royal Barge, 1895

1895•
ROYAL BARGE *Burma*
Since ancient times, royalty have liked to ride in fine barges on ceremonial occasions. This royal barge was used on the Irrawaddy River by the King of Burma, who sat in the raised area in the middle. It was richly decorated, to remind people of his power and wealth, and rowed by oarsmen in colourful costumes.

•1897 *TURBINIA* Britain
A new era began when Charles Parsons' ship *Turbinia* achieved the astonishing speed of 34.5 knots (64 kph/40 mph), thanks to a special type of engine called a steam turbine. Lighter than ordinary steam engines, the turbine used a jet of steam to turn a set of blades attached to the propeller shaft.

Turbinia, 1897

•**1890** The world's first electric "tube" railway opens in London, England. It runs inside a tunnel bored deep under the River Thames.
•**1890** In France, Clément Ader's *Éole* is the first full-sized, person-carrying aeroplane to take off under its own power.
•**1890** In Scotland, the massive Forth railway bridge is completed.
•**1891** Frenchmen Emile Levassor and René Panhard design the first car to have its engine at the front, driving the rear wheels through a clutch and gearbox.

•**1891** In Germany, Otto Lilienthal makes the first of a series of experimental glider flights.
•**1892** The escalator is invented by Jesse Reno in the USA.
•**1892** In Germany, Rudolph Diesel patents a new internal combustion engine. Diesel engines will become standard for all heavy road vehicles.
•**1893** The Duryea brothers of Springfield, Massachusetts, build the USA's first successful petrol car.
•**1893** Australian Lawrence Hargrave invents the box kite, which will influence later aeroplane designers.

The Paris Métro

•**1895** The Kiel Canal is completed in Germany, providing a shipping route between the Baltic and North seas.
•**1895** The world's first official road race for cars takes place in France, from Paris to Bordeaux and back.
•**1895** A main-line electric railway service starts on a stretch of the USA's Baltimore and Ohio Railroad.
•**1896** Britain's Red Flag Act is repealed, allowing vehicles a top speed of 19 kph (12 mph). See **MILESTONES 1865**.

•**1897** The first Stanley steam car is made in the USA.
•**1897** With the success of Charles Parsons' turbine-driven *Turbinia*, steam turbines begin to be adopted for most ships.
•**1898** In Paris, France, work starts on an underground railway system or "Métro". It will open in 1900.
•**1899** Camille Jenatzy, a Belgian, sets a world speed record of 106 kph (66 mph) in an electric car.

1900

1905

| 1900 | 1901 | | 1903 | 1904 | 1905 | 1906 | 1907 | 1908 | 1909 |

AIR

•1903 WRIGHT *FLYER* USA
The first successful aeroplane flight was made by Orville Wright in the *Flyer* on 17 December, 1903. Crucial to this success was the use of a petrol engine to power the *Flyer*. Orville and his brother Wilbur had experimented with gliders, which taught them how an aeroplane could be controlled in flight. On its first flight, the *Flyer* travelled 37 m (120 ft) in 12 seconds.

Langley's *Aerodrome*, 1901

•1901 LANGLEY'S *AERODROME* USA
The American scientist Samuel Langley built a series of model aeroplanes that he called *Aerodromes*. His 1901 tandem-winged version (wings one behind the other) eventually achieved a 300-m (1,000-ft) flight, and was the first successful petrol-engined flying machine. But a full-sized, person-carrying version crashed when attempting take-off, and was abandoned.

Orville Wright makes the first flight in the *Flyer*, 1903

Upper rudder

Horizontal fin

Handling guy ropes

Lower rudder

Propeller

Rear passenger car

The arm collects electricity from an overhead wire.

Steering wheel

Horn bulb

Folding windscreen

Rear seat

Front seat

Mudguard

Radiator filler cap

Folding hood

LAND

Model of London electric tram, 1901

1901•
ELECTRIC TRAM *Britain*
For millions of city dwellers, electric trams provided a faster and cheaper alternative to the horse-drawn bus or tram. Taking their power from cables overhead, electric trams carried no fuel, and did not pollute the streets as horses did and as motor buses do today. Most electric trams ran on rails embedded in the street.

•1903
TANK LOCOMOTIVE
Chile
A tank locomotive carries its own fuel and water, so it has no tender. To climb steep gradients in the rugged Andes region of Chile, this locomotive had two power units, each with its own cylinders and chimney, fed with steam from a single boiler in the middle. To get around tight corners, it is "articulated", with its wheels mounted on swivelling bogies.

Model of a Kitson–Meyer tank locomotive built for use in Chile, 1903

Side view of Model T Ford, 1914

Running board

Pneumatic tyres

1908•
FORD MODEL T *USA*
First sold in 1908, Henry Ford's Model T was rugged, reliable, and easy to drive. In 1913, it became the first car to be mass-produced on a moving assembly line. At the peak of production, up to 1,000 cars left the factory each day, bringing the price down to a level ordinary people could afford. The inflexible assembly-line method led Henry Ford to say that the car could be had in any colour – so long as it was black! Nicknamed the "Tin Lizzie", the Model T's top speed was 70 kph (45 mph).

Wing mirror

Front view of Model T Ford, 1914

Headlight

Material from the riverbed is sent down the chute into barges alongside.

Front axle

Starting handle

BE 2789

WATER

•1901
DREDGER *Britain*
As ships became larger, they needed wider and deeper channels to get into harbours and up rivers, so there was plenty of work for specialized vessels called dredgers. Some sucked up a watery mixture of mud or sand from the bottom. Others used an endless chain of buckets to scrape up clay and gravel and bring it to the surface. Anchors, or a series of ropes or wires tied to the banks, kept the dredger in place as it worked.

The wheel turns the chain of buckets.

Model of *St. Enoch*, 1901, a non-ocean-going dredger

Radio aerial

•1907 *MAURETANIA* Britain
On the transatlantic route, where speed and comfort were important, the newest liners were now powered by steam turbine engines. *Mauretania*'s four turbines used 1,000 tonnes of coal a day to take it from Liverpool, England, to New York, USA, in less than five days. *Mauretania* was the first ship to use a radio receiver to take navigational bearings.

MILESTONES

| 1900–1904 | | 1905–1909 | |

Mechanism to raise or lower the chain of buckets as the tide changes

•1901 In France, the Werner brothers design a motorcycle with the engine where the pedals are on a normal bicycle. This will become the standard design for all motorcycles.
•1901 A commercial "monorail" (a railway with only one rail) starts at Wuppertal, Germany. Its electric trains hang from a single, elevated rail.
•1901 In the USA, Ransom Olds uses mass-production methods in his car factory, which will soon make 5,000 "Oldsmobiles" a year.
•1903 Orville Wright makes his historic first flight at Kitty Hawk, North Carolina, USA.
•1904 A French engineer, Eugène Freysinnet, invents "pre-stressed concrete", which will be essential for building bridges later this century.

•1900 Battery-powered "electric broughams", named after a horse-drawn carriage, will be popular in the USA as personal transport for the next 20 years.
•1900 In Germany, Count Ferdinand von Zeppelin tries out the first of his enormous rigid airships. His company will build more than 100 "Zeppelins" over the next 30 years.

•1905 Motor buses appear in New York, USA, and in London, England, where they will completely replace horse-drawn buses by 1914.

Blériot's cross-Channel flight, 1909

•1907 The luxury turbine-powered British liner *Lusitania* (sister ship of the *Mauretania*) enters service. It is the largest and fastest afloat, but will be sunk by a German submarine in 1915.
•1907 The first successful aeroplane flight in Europe is made by the English-born, French-speaking Henri Farman in his *Voisin-Farman 1*. The flight lasts just over one minute.
•1908 The Ford Motor Company introduces its Model T car. It will sell 16.5 million by 1927.
•1908 Thérèse Peltier is the first woman to fly in an aeroplane.
•1909 Louis Blériot makes the first aeroplane flight across the English Channel in his Type XI monoplane, and wins a prize of £1,000.

1910   1915

| 1910 | 1911 | 1912 | 1913 | 1914 | 1915 | 1916 |

Model of
Schütte-Lanz
SL1 rigid
airship, 1911

Nose

*Forward
passenger car
and flight deck*

•1911
RIGID AIRSHIP
Germany

The largest airships were
"rigids", made of stretched
cloth over a framework of light metal or wood. Hydrogen-filled
gas bags inside the airship gave the lifting force. More than 150
rigids were built between 1900 and 1938. Up to 200 m (650 ft)
long and powered by internal combustion engines, they carried
passengers on long-distance flights. Some were
used to bomb cities during World War I.
Hydrogen burns easily, and many
rigids were lost in fires.

*Sober grey paint-
work contributed
to the bike's name*

Headlight

Silent Gray Fellow, 1912

*Pedals are used to
start the engine and
set the motorcycle in
motion, because it has
no starter or gearbox.*

•1912 HARLEY DAVIDSON *USA*

Motorcycles had already evolved into their modern shape when William
Harley and the three Davidson brothers began making them in Wisconsin,
USA, in 1903. Motorcycles were more affordable than cars, and Harley-
Davidson machines such as the single cylinder Silent Gray Fellow were
soon contributing to a boom in sales. Its top speed was 72 kph (45 mph).

1915•
ALL-METAL MONOPLANE *Germany*

At a time when most aircraft were still mainly built of
wood, Hugo Junkers in Germany designed his all-metal
J1 monoplane. Its revolutionary steel wings were fully
cantilevered – that is, built straight out from the body of
the aircraft, with no extra wires or struts to support them.
With its streamlined exterior, the J1 achieved a speed of
170 kph (105 mph), and was the first
of a line of successful Junkers aircraft.

**Junkers J1, 1915 – the world's
first all-metal aeroplane**

•1916
TANK *Britain/France*

In World War I, British and French
engineers developed armoured
vehicles that ran on metal "caterpillar"
tracks. These tracks enabled the vehicles to
cross rough ground by laying down their own
metal "road" and picking it up behind them. To
hide its real purpose from the enemy, the British
referred to their vehicle as a "water tank", and
the name has stuck.

**British tank,
1916**

**LVG C.VI,
1917**

•1917
RECONNAISSANCE FIGHTER *Germany*

With the outbreak of World War I in 1914,
thousands of new aircraft were produced. Many were
reconnaissance fighters, such as the German LVG
C.VI. Their role was to observe and photograph
enemy activity. They were
equipped with machine
guns to defend themselves
or attack other aircraft.

K type bus, 1919–32

1919•
MOTOR BUS *Britain*

By placing the driver alongside the
engine instead of behind it, the
designers of the AEC K type
double-decker produced a version
of the famous red London bus that
could seat 46 passengers. Forward-
facing seats inside were another
innovation, but upstairs passengers
were still unprotected from the
weather, and the bus ran on solid
rubber tyres, not pneumatic ones.

**Model of the luxury
liner *Mauretania*, 1907**

Lifeboat

*Swivelling
gun turret*

•1915 BATTLESHIP *Germany*

Powerful and heavily armoured battleships controlled the
oceans during World War I. Earlier warships carried
their guns along each side (*see* **WARSHIP 1511**),
but battleships now carried their weaponry
on deck. The guns were mounted in pairs
in swivelling turrets along the ship's
centre-line, so that its formidable
fire-power could be pointed in
any direction.

**Model of the
German
battleship
Baden, 1915**

US destroyer, 1917

•1917 DESTROYER *USA*

A destroyer's role in World War I was to
protect other ships, particularly from attack
by a new and very destructive weapon – the
torpedo. This was an underwater missile,
usually launched from a submarine.
Destroyers (originally called "torpedo-boat
destroyers") were smaller and faster than
battleships, and carried their own guns and
torpedo-launching equipment.

| 1910–1914 | | 1915–1919 | |

•**1910** Frenchman Henri Fabre
builds a "seaplane" – an aeroplane
that can take off and land on water.
•**1911** In the USA, a white line is
used to mark the centre of roads.
•**1911** In India, 6,500 letters are
carried by aeroplane – probably the
world's first official air mail delivery.
•**1912** The liner *Titanic*, the largest
ever launched, hits an iceberg and
sinks with the loss of 1,513 lives.
•**1912** In the USA, electric starters
are now standard in all Cadillac
cars. Other cars are still started by
turning a crank handle at the front.

•**1912** SOS is now a universal
distress signal for ships and aircraft.
•**1913** Travel from Europe to the
Far East takes less than two weeks
on the Trans-Siberian Railway.
•**1913** Ford assembles Model T
cars on a moving conveyor belt.
•**1913** Grand Central railway
station – the largest in the world –
opens in New York, USA.
•**1914** The world's first traffic
lights are used in Cleveland, USA.
•**1914** The 82-km (51-mile)
Panama Canal opens, linking the
Atlantic and Pacific Oceans.

The sinking of the *Titanic*, 1912

• **1915** A Hawaiian introduces
surfboarding to Australia, where
it soon becomes popular.
•**1915** German airships drop
bombs on Britain.
•**1915** The German Junkers J1
is the first all-metal aeroplane.
•**1916** Some American cars are
fitted with vacuum-operated
windscreen wipers. Electric
wipers will follow soon in 1923.
•**1917** A railway is completed
across Australia. It has a 480-km
(300-mile) stretch without a
single bend.

•**1919** The first non-stop flight
across the Atlantic is made by
British aviators John Alcock and
Arthur Whitten-Brown in a
Vickers Vimy "biplane" (a two-
winged aircraft). The journey
from Newfoundland takes 16.5
hours, and ends safely with a
crash-landing in an Irish bog. Two
weeks later, the British airship R34
also makes a non-stop crossing.
•**1919** Daily passenger flights are
set up between London, England,
and Paris, France. This is the first
regular international service.

1920

1925

| 1920 | 1921 | 1924 | 1925 | 1926 | 1927 |

AIR

Rotor blade

Cierva C-30, 1932

A conventional propeller at the front pulls the aircraft forward for take-off and normal flight.

Fuselage of steel tubing covered with fabric

The autogiro's upswept tailplane keeps the fuselage steady. It counter-balances the force created by the rotor blade overhead.

•1923•
AUTOGIRO *Spain/Britain*
An autogiro is a small aeroplane with no wings. It is pulled forward by a motor-driven propeller at the front. The large overhead rotor is not turned by its own motor – as on a helicopter – but is blown around as the autogiro moves forward. This lifts the autogiro off the ground. The first autogiro was made by the Spaniard Juan de la Cierva in 1923.

•1926•
RACING SEAPLANE *Italy*
Streamlined racing seaplanes, designed to take off and land on water, took part each year in the international Schneider Trophy contest. First place in the 1926 race went to Italy's Macchi M.39, whose 600-kW (800-hp) Fiat engine gave it a top speed of 420 kph (260 mph). The winner of the 1931 Trophy, the Supermarine S6B, was the forerunner of Britain's successful Spitfire fighter.
See **FIGHTERS AND BOMBERS 1940–45.**

Macchi M.39, 1926 Schneider Trophy winner

The flying doctor makes a call

•1928•
FLYING DOCTOR *Australia*
Two new technologies, the light aeroplane and the two-way radio, have come together to provide emergency medical care in sparsely populated parts of the world. Since 1928, Australia's Royal Flying Doctor Service has been a lifeline for people living in isolated areas. The first flying doctor, Dr. K. St. Vincent Welch, flew in a small de Havilland DH–50 aircraft. In its first year, the service treated 255 patients.

LAND

1926•
MOTOR COACH *Britain*
People who did not have their own cars could still enjoy the delights of motoring on a country outing by coach – a motorized version of the horse-drawn "charabanc" (French for "carriage with benches"). Some motor charabancs wisely incorporated a folding hood that could quickly be raised to protect the passengers if it started to rain.

Charabanc, 1926

•1923 DIESEL TRUCK** *Germany*
Transporting goods by road became easier when the Benz company introduced its first diesel-powered truck, designed in 1923 and made commercially available in 1924. Diesel engines are more powerful, run on cheaper fuel, and do more kilometres to the litre than petrol engines. By the 1930s, a large number of goods vehicles had diesel engines.

Benz diesel truck, 1923

•1928•
MOTO GUZZI 500S *Italy*
Motorcycles were at their most popular during the 1920s and 1930s, when they met the needs of many people who could not afford a car. The Italian Moto Guzzi company was a leading producer of motorcycles in the 1920s. The design of the single-cylinder 500 cc Moto Guzzi was so advanced that it stayed in production for more than 50 years. The S model was one of the more basic versions.

Moto Guzzi 500S, 1928

WATER

Model of *København* training and cargo ship, 1921

•1921•
SAILING BARQUE *Denmark*
The last large sailing ships were built in the early part of the 20th century. Many were steel-hulled "barques" (or "barks"), which were economical to run because their rigging could be handled by a fairly small crew. The Danish *København* was a five-masted barque used for young sailors. It also carried cargo to subsidize the cost of training.

•1924 OIL TANKER** *Britain*
As demand for petrol grew, specialized ships called oil tankers were used to transport crude oil and the products made from it. As with all tankers up until the 1990s, the hull of the 6,000-tonne *Wellfield*, shown below, was basically a large floating tank, with compartments into which the oil was poured.

Model of the oil tanker *Wellfield*, 1924

The submarine was driven by propellers at the stern.

Tanks in the hull took in water to make the submarine dive, and expelled water to make the submarine rise to the surface.

The crew's quarters and the 450-kW (600-hp) diesel engine were at the stern of the ship.

MILESTONES

1920–1929

•**1920** The British ship *Fullagar* is the first to be built from metal plates that are welded together rather than riveted.
•**1920** The American Dayton-Wright RB racing monoplane is the first with a retractable undercarriage.
•**1921** In the USA, the Duesenberg Model A is the first car with hydraulic brakes. Pressure on the brake pedal is transmitted to the wheels through tubes filled with liquid.
•**1921** American chemists discover that adding a compound called tetraethyl lead to petrol reduces "knocking" (premature explosion) in car engines.

•**1923** The Bronx River Parkway opens in the USA – the first ever limited-access highway. Motorists can join or leave it only at specially built interchanges.
•**1923** The German government plans a major road-building programme that will complete 3,300 km (2,050 miles) of motorways or "autobahns" by 1939.
•**1923** Britain's *Hermes* and Japan's *Hosho* are the world's first purpose-built aircraft carriers.
•**1924** The first round-the-world flight is made by two Douglas biplanes. The aircraft travel 44,000 km (27,600 miles) over a period of 5.5 months.

Robert Goddard beside his rocket, 1926

•**1926** The American scientist Robert Goddard launches the first successful liquid-fuel rocket. Its 2.5 second flight reaches a height of 12.5 m (41 ft).
•**1927** British driver Henry Seagrave reaches 328 kph (204 mph) in his *Sunbeam* car.
•**1927** Charles Lindbergh makes the first solo non-stop transatlantic flight in his Ryan monoplane *Spirit of St. Louis*.
•**1927** The USA's Fageol Twin Coach sets a new style in bus design, with its flat front and driver-operated doors.
•**1927** Japan's first underground railway opens in Tokyo.

•**1928** In Britain, Frank Whittle has the idea of using jet propulsion for aircraft, but will not build his first jet engine until 1937.
•**1928** A transcontinental bus service operates across the USA. It uses "nite coaches" with sleeping facilities.
•**1929** General Motors introduces the synchromesh gearbox on its Cadillac cars. Synchromesh eventually becomes standard, making gear-changing easier.
•**1929** The airship *Graf Zeppelin* flies around the world in 21 days.
•**1929** Five million new cars are made in the USA this year.

1930 1935

Flight deck

Boeing 247D, 1933

Landing gear folds into wing after take-off

410-kW (550-hp) air-cooled radial engine

Propeller blades swivel to give the right angle, or "pitch", for take-off, landing, or cruising

•1933 BOEING 247 *USA*
As new airliners were developed, flying began to be an everyday means of transport for many people, especially in the USA. The twin-engined Boeing 247 could whisk its ten passengers over a distance of 1,000 km (600 miles) in only four hours. Its novel features included an all-metal skin, and wheels that could be pulled up into the wings to reduce drag when the plane was airborne.

•1935 DOUGLAS DC3 *USA*
No airliner has sold in such large numbers as the Douglas DC3, which carried up to 21 passengers at 270 kph (170 mph). By 1939, these dependable aircraft had become the "workhorses" of the skies, transporting 90 per cent of all airline passengers. The DC3, later renamed "Skytrain" or "Dakota", went on to provide vital services during World War II and after.

A Douglas DC3, still in service in 1981

Heinkel 178, 1939

**1939•
JET AIRCRAFT**
Germany
There is a limit to how fast a propeller-driven aeroplane can travel, so designers looking for speed turned to another type of engine – the turbojet. The earliest pioneer was the German engineer Hans von Ohain, who installed a jet engine in the experimental Heinkel 178. It flew successfully in August 1939, and later achieved the spectacular speed of 755 kph (470 mph).

The high bonnet conceals a powerful 4.5-litre engine.

Greyhound bus, 1931

**•1931
INTERCITY BUS** *USA*
Improved roads in the USA led to the setting up of many intercity bus routes. By 1931, the Greyhound bus companies had a 65,000-km (40,000-mile) network linking cities and beauty spots in the USA, Mexico, and Canada. Since the 1930s, intercity buses have provided a comfortable and cheap form of public transport over long distances.

**1934•
STREAMLINER TRAIN** *USA*
Futuristic-looking streamlined trains were introduced on long-distance lines in the USA, hauled not by steam locomotives but by diesel-electrics. Streamliners were popular for their speed as well as their comfort, particularly after Union Pacific's air-conditioned M–10001 train crossed the continent from San Francisco to New York in a record time of only 57 hours.

**Union Pacific M–10000
City of Salina, 1934**

Golf-club hatch | **Side view of Auburn 851 Speedster, 1935**

"Whitewall" tyres

V-shaped radiator grill

•1935 SPORTS CAR *USA*
American cars of the 1930s were often large, powerful, and stylish. Like the Auburn 851 Speedster, many of them were designed more to impress than to be practical motor vehicles. The Auburn was 6 m (20 ft) long, but was only a two-seater and had little room for luggage – although it did have a special locker for stowing golf clubs!

Front view of Auburn 851 Speedster, 1935

Model of U-25: launched 1936, sunk 1940

**•1936
U-BOAT** *Germany*
Submarines proved even more deadly in World War II than they had in World War I. A fleet of German U-boats – short for "Unterseebooten" (undersea boats) – was developed from prototypes like the one shown here. U-25 carried 14 torpedoes and could remain submerged for long periods. On the move, it had to resurface every 125 km (78 miles) to replenish its air supplies.

**1939•
BATTLESHIP** *Germany*
With eight huge guns, the German battleship *Bismarck* was a threat to Atlantic shipping routes in World War II. Launched in 1939, *Bismarck* was sunk by gunfire and torpedoes from British ships and aircraft in 1941. By the end of the war, aircraft carriers had become more important than battleships in naval warfare.
See **AIRCRAFT CARRIER 1946.**

Model of *Bismarck*, 1939

The "conning tower" gives a good viewing position when the submarine is on the surface.

Fins on each side of the hull swivel to deflect the flow of water, raising or lowering the submarine's nose.

•1930 STEAM TUG *Britain*
Tugs are small, powerful boats used to manoeuvre large ships into and out of dock, and for pushing or pulling long chains of river barges. The large funnel reflects the power of the huge steam or diesel engine that fills much of a tug's hull space. Tugs are also used for fire fighting, and for helping broken down or damaged ships.

Model of a steam tug, c.1930

1930–1939

• **1930s** Heavy lorries, often with 6 or 8 wheels to carry bigger loads, are a common sight on many roads.
• **1930s** Steam locomotives are beginning to give way to diesels and main-line electric services.
• **1930** The German Society for Space Travel opens a site near Berlin to build and test liquid-fuel rockets.
• **1930** Amy Johnson flies solo from Britain to Australia in 19 days.
• **1931** The British Supermarine S6B seaplane wins the international Schneider Trophy race, averaging 547.3 kph (340.1 mph).

• **1932** The Sydney Harbour Bridge opens in Australia. It carries a dual railway track, two footpaths, and a road, all suspended from a steel arch.
• **1932** Amelia Earhart becomes the first woman to fly the Atlantic solo.
• **1933** The twin-engined Boeing 247 is the first modern-style airliner.
• **1934** In the USA, a streamlined diesel-electric train called the *Pioneer Zephyr* runs non-stop for 1,633 km (1,015 miles) between Denver and Chicago.

The giant *Hindenburg* airship bursts into flames while docking, 1937

• **1935** The first parking meters are introduced in Oklahoma City, USA.
• **1935** The Boeing B-17, or "Flying Fortress", is the first four-engined, all metal, monoplane bomber.
• **1935** The Moscow underground railway opens.
• **1935** The French liner *Normandie* crosses the Atlantic in a record time of 4 days, 3 hours, and 2 minutes.
• **1935** The Scottish scientist Robert Watson-Watt uses radio waves to detect aircraft. Radar will become vital for tracking ships and aircraft, and for navigation.

• **1935** In the USA, the Douglas DC3 makes it first flight.
• **1936** In Germany, prototypes are made of the Volkswagen "Beetle".
• **1937** The Golden Gate Bridge opens in San Francisco, USA. For 30 years it will be the longest suspension bridge in the world.
• **1937** The age of the passenger airship ends when the *Hindenburg* explodes in New Jersey, USA.
• **1938** The Boeing 307 is the first airliner with a pressurized cabin.
• **1939** The German Heinkel 178 is the first jet-propelled aircraft.

1940

1940	1941

1945

1945	1946	1947	1948	1949

AIR

Supermarine Spitfire and Messerschmitt Me 109

•1940–45 FIGHTERS AND BOMBERS

In the mid-air "dogfights" of World War II, the performance of a fighter-plane's engine was almost as crucial as its weapons or the skill of its pilot. British Spitfire and Hurricane fighters had Rolls-Royce engines, while Daimler-Benz engines powered Germany's Messerschmitts. Bombers, too, needed powerful engines – and more of them – in order to carry huge bomb loads for the "saturation" bombing of cities and other targets. America's Boeing B-17 Flying Fortress bomber had four 900-kW (1,200-hp) Wright Cyclone engines, two on each wing.

Boeing B-17 Flying Fortress

•1943 LOCKHEED CONSTELLATION USA

First used for military transport, Lockheed's four-engined Constellation entered service as a commercial airliner after World War II. With a range of 3,200 km (2,000 miles), it could carry up to 81 passengers at 550 kph (340 mph). The Constellation played an important part in the rapid growth of air travel in the 1950s.

Lockheed Constellation in service in Brazil, 1949

•1945 HELICOPTER USA

Modern helicopters follow a design pioneered in 1942 by Igor Sikorsky, a Russian-American. His XR–4 helicopter had a large rotor, like an upturned propeller, that raised the helicopter off the ground. The rotor was tilted to move the helicopter forwards or backwards. A tail rotor acted like a rudder, and stopped the aircraft from spinning around.

Sikorsky R–4 helicopter, 1945

Pilot's seat

Front landing wheel

Engine housing

The fins, designed to look like aircraft tailplanes, were purely decorative.

Huge chromed bumper

Citroën 2CV, 1949

1949• CITROËN 2CV France

With its tiny engine and "garden-shed" bodywork, Citroën's 2CV was designed as a first car for people in France's rural areas. Although many of its drivers were farmers more used to travelling by horse and cart, they soon found it remarkably spacious and robust.

LAND

1941• BIG BOY USA

To haul huge freight trains across the Rocky Mountains, the Union Pacific Railroad built the largest ever steam locomotives. Known as "Big Boys", these 40-m (130-ft) long giants had a top speed of 130 kph (80 mph), making them fast as well as powerful. Clouds of black smoke poured from their chimneys, because the exhaust contained large amounts of unburned coal particles.

A Big Boy locomotive in steam, 1940s

•1944 JEEP USA

The US Army's General Purpose vehicle (GP or "jeep" for short), was designed for battlefield reconnaissance duties. But it was soon being used as an emergency ambulance, a mobile gun platform, and in many other roles. Jeeps were light enough to be carried in a glider and dropped by parachute, or delivered to beaches in small landing craft.

A jeep emerges from a landing craft, 1944

WATER

1941• LIBERTY SHIP USA

In four years during World War II, more than 2,700 cargo steamers were mass-produced in the USA to replace ships being sunk by German, Italian, and Japanese submarines. These "Liberty ships" followed a simple, rugged design, using prefabricated parts and a welded steel hull. One ship was built in the record time of 14 days from start to finish.

Studebaker "Water Weasel" amphibious cargo carrier, 1944

"Derrick" lifts cargo on and off ship

Model of a Liberty ship, 1941

•1944 AMPHIBIOUS VEHICLE USA

When the Studebaker company added a boat-like body, two rudders, and flotation tanks to its "Weasel" military vehicle, it produced a version that travelled both in water and on land. The amphibious "Water Weasel" had rubber tracks for moving over difficult surfaces such as snow. Its top speed was 58 kph (36 mph) on land, but only 6 kph (4 mph) in water.

1946• AIRCRAFT CARRIER Britain

HMS *Eagle* served in the British Navy for 26 years. Aircraft carriers have changed the nature of sea warfare, because their aircraft can attack targets beyond the range of any warship's guns. During take-off, the aircraft are propelled forward by a device called a "catapult", while "arrester" wires across the deck slow them as they land.

Many aircraft used on aircraft carriers have wings that fold up to save space on deck.

Radar aerial to identify and track targets

Cranes lift aircraft out of water if they overshoot flight deck

Model of HMS Eagle (1946–72) as it looked in 1964

MILESTONES

1940–1949

•**1940** Igor Sikorsky's VS-300 is the world's first practical single rotor helicopter.
•**1940** A four-wheel drive General Purpose car (or "jeep") is designed for the US Army.

B-12 snowmobile, early 1940s

•**1941** "Big Boy" locomotives enter service on America's Union Pacific Railway.
•**1941** In Canada, the Bombardier company introduces the versatile B-12, one of the most successful snowmobiles ever.
•**1941** The first Liberty ship is launched in the USA.
•**1942** Germany's Messerschmitt Me 262 jet fighter makes its first flight, followed in 1943 by the British Gloster Meteor jet.
•**1944** Germany launches the first of nearly 3,000 V2 armed rockets at targets in Britain and elsewhere.

Liquid-fuelled V2 rocket, 1944

•**1945** An American Boeing B-29 bomber drops the first atomic bomb on the Japanese city of Hiroshima.
•**1946** Motorized scooters called "Vespas" (Italian for wasp) appear in Italy.
•**1946** In New Mexico, USA, a rocket is fired to a height of 80 km (50 miles). US rocket engineers also begin experimenting with captured V2 rockets. *See* MILESTONES 1944.
•**1947** As demand for petrol rises, drilling for undersea oil starts in the Gulf of Mexico.

•**1947** Captain "Chuck" Yeager breaks the sound barrier in the Bell X1 rocket-plane. At an altitude of 12,800 m (42,000 ft) he reaches a speed of 1,078 kph (670 mph) – faster than the speed of sound at that height.
•**1947** Soichiro Honda fits war-surplus engines to ordinary bicycles in Japan. By 1960, his Honda company will be the world's leading producer of motorcycles.
1949 A US B-50A bomber flies non-stop around the world, refuelling in mid-air four times in the course of its 94-hour flight.
•**1949** The Citroën 2CV car appears in France. People laugh at its odd appearance, but millions will be sold around the world.

1950

1955

Large rotor blade lifted helicopter off ground

Tail rotor acts as rudder and stops helicopter from spinning around

Boom

Rear landing wheel

Electrically operated windows

•1952
DE HAVILLAND COMET *Britain*
The first jet airliner was the sleek 48-passenger de Havilland Comet 1, which had four turbojet engines mounted in its wings. The Comet 1's structural weaknesses led to a number of crashes. The improved Comet 4 became the first jet in transatlantic service.

DH Comet Mark 4, 1958

Aircraft-style "wrap-around" windscreen

Rocket-style bonnet mascot

•1958
BOEING 707 *USA*
The classic shape of jet airliners was set by the Boeing 707, with its four jet engines slung below swept-back wings. Its success was largely responsible for the change from propeller-driven to jet airliners. The 707 cruised at 880 kph (550 mph), carried up to 190 passengers, and had a range of 6,900 km (4,300 miles).

Prototype Boeing 707, 1958

Cadillac Coupé de Ville, 1957

Stylized chrome-plated hub cap

•1957
CADILLAC COUPÉ DE VILLE *USA*
American cars of the 1950s were long, low, wide, and enormously powerful. "Dreamboats" such as the Cadillac Coupé de Ville were as much an expression of the owner's status and personality as a practical means of transport. Petrol was cheap, so people were not worried about the high fuel consumption of these "gas-guzzler" cars.

c.1950 CABLE TRAMCAR *USA*
Nearly 80 years after they were introduced, San Francisco's cable tramcars were on the way to becoming one of the USA's National Historic Landmarks. Cable tramcars operate by grabbing a moving cable running under the street. They were once used in many cities, particularly where steep hills caused problems for other types of tram.

San Francisco tramcar, c.1950

1957•
LAMBRETTA SCOOTER *Italy*
In the years following World War II, the motor scooter helped meet the need for cheap, economical forms of transport. With its small wheels and a platform for the rider's feet, a scooter is easier to ride than a full-size motorcycle. Scooters first became popular in Italy, where the Lambretta was a leading model.

Lambretta LD 150, 1957

Aircraft stored below deck in hangars and brought up by a lift

•1951 RECYCLED SHIP *Sweden*
Launched as an oil tanker in 1951, *John E. Hyde* was converted to carry grain, metal ores, and other dry cargo that can be loaded "in bulk" (loose). The hull was enlarged and the "holds" – compartments below deck – were strengthened. Only large ships can undergo such a transformation, as it involves cutting the ship in halves, both lengthways and widthways, and adding extra sections.

Model of John E. Hyde as dry cargo ship

Separate holds stop cargo from shifting in rough seas.

1959•
NUCLEAR SHIP *USA*
Savannah was the first merchant ship to be powered by a nuclear reactor, which enabled it to go 3.5 years without refuelling. The reactor produced heat by splitting atoms. The heat was then used to generate steam to power turbines. Only a few nuclear-powered merchant ships have been built, because they are so expensive to build and operate.

•1955
HOVERCRAFT *Britain*
Hovercraft ride on a cushion of high-pressure air that reduces friction between the craft and the surface over which it travels. In 1955, the British engineer Christopher Cockerell made a successful model hovercraft powered by a model aeroplane engine. The world's first full-sized hovercraft, Cockerell's SR-N1, made its first appearance in 1959.

Anti-aircraft guns to defend against enemy aircraft

Cockerell's SR–N1 hovercraft, 1959

Model of NS *Savannah*, launched 1959

1950–1954

•**1951** The Chrysler Imperial is the first car with power-assisted steering, which uses power from the engine to help turn the steering wheel.
•**1952** The world's first jet airliner, the de Havilland Comet 1, enters service.
•**1953** The Chevrolet Corvette is the first production car to have a plastic body, made from reinforced fibreglass.

Surfing in the 1950s

•**1953** The ancestor of modern surfboards, the polyurethane plastic "Simmons board" (or "Malibu board"), goes on sale.
•**1953** The first turboprop airliner, the Vickers Viscount, goes into service. Turboprop engines use a gas turbine to drive a propeller.
•**1954** In Britain, a curious machine nicknamed the "Flying Bedstead" shows that jet aircraft will one day be able to take off vertically by directing their engines' thrust downwards.

1955–1959

•**1955** The American submarine *Nautilus* is the first to be powered by a nuclear reactor.
•**1956** The world's first regular hydrofoil service starts between Sicily and mainland Italy.
•**1957** The Soviet Union's *Sputnik 1* is the first artificial satellite to orbit the Earth. A dog called Laika aboard *Sputnik 2* becomes the first living creature in space.
•**1958** Austin's Mini-Minor goes on sale. It will be Britain's best-selling car ever.
•**1958** The Boeing 707, one of the worlds most successful jet airliners, enters service.

•**1959** Seat belts are offered as an optional extra on cars from the Swedish manufacturer Volvo.
•**1959** In England, Christopher Cockerell designs the world's first practical hovercraft.
•**1959** The St. Lawrence Seaway opens, allowing ships from the Atlantic to travel 3,800 km (2,400 miles) into the Great Lakes region of North America.
•**1959** The Russian icebreaker *Lenin* is the first non-military ship to have a nuclear reactor.

Laika – the first living creature in space, 1957

1960–2000 A world on the move

S PACE TRAVEL WAS FOR MANY YEARS something that people only read about in books and comics, or saw in science fiction movies. Then, in the 1960s, it suddenly became real. A Russian cosmonaut orbited the Earth in space in 1961; eight years later, American astronauts were walking on the Moon. But manned space flight proved enormously expensive, and after 1972, no more journeys to the Moon or planets were planned. Space travellers stayed nearer to home, orbiting the Earth in the USA's reusable Space Shuttle or making visits to the Soviet space station *Mir*. Unmanned satellites brought benefits such as better communications between continents, while robot spacecraft sent back photographs that greatly increased our knowledge of the distant planets. Back on Earth, the use of motor vehicles continued to grow rapidly throughout the world, while the introduction of larger-capacity "jumbo jets" gave a huge boost to air travel.

Vostok rocket

Apollo 11's "Buzz" Aldrin on the Moon, 1969

THE SPACE AGE
In 1969, millions of people shared the thrill of humanity's first footsteps on another world, watching live television broadcasts and poring over newspaper reports of the *Apollo 11* mission. It had only been a few short years since the Soviet *Vostok 1* rocket lifted the first person, Yuri Gagarin, into space. Soon there were space stations orbiting the Earth, and robot craft landing on Mars. Pictures of the Earth in space reminded people that our planet is itself a sort of spaceship, with a fragile environment.

Transport and the consumer society

In the years after 1960, freight transport of all kinds increased as consumers in richer countries got a taste for goods, such as electrical equipment and cars, that had to be imported from factories thousands of miles away. Similarly, most people in 1900 ate food that had been grown close to where they lived, but by the 1980s shoppers expected to find exotic foreign fruit and vegetables in their supermarkets all year round. These demands could only be met by more cargo boats and freight aircraft, and heavier "juggernaut" lorries pounding down the motorways at home.

The solar panels convert the energy of the Sun's rays into electricity to power the space station's systems and machinery.

A Soyuz TM spacecraft docks with Mir, carrying a relief crew for the space station.

As many as six spacecraft can dock here at the same time. Cosmonauts enter and leave the space station via an air lock.

Soviet Soyuz TM spacecraft, first launched 1986

THE CHANGING WORLD: 1960 to 2000

Wheel covering makes design more aerodynamic

Composite frame of carbon-fibre, fibreglass, and epoxy resin

Windcheater Carbon Cantilever

NEW MATERIALS
Sport has made the most of the new high-tech materials. Some of the fastest bicycles have frames made of plastic reinforced with carbon-fibre, which is twice as rigid as steel. Titanium metal is used for wheel bearings, because it is as strong as steel but much lighter. Plastic reinforced with fibreglass is used to make racing car bodies and hulls for yachts and canoes, while skis and bobsleighs are coated with the low-friction plastic PTFE.

SAFETY FIRST
As the number of road deaths increased, public pressure grew for manufacturers to build cars that would give motorists greater protection in an accident. Safety fittings included seat belts and air bags, which inflate instantly to cushion a driver in a crash. Engineers learned to build safer roads, and law-makers brought in new rules and tougher penalties for bad drivers.

Testing air bags

Swedish X–2000 tilting train, 1990

RAIL REVIVAL
Railways have fought back against the aeroplane and the car. New electric services such as the French TGVs and the Japanese Shinkansen routes provide standards of speed and comfort to rival those of airliners. For trains as fast as these, new track without sharp bends often has to be laid. Alternatively, trains can be built with bodies that "lean" or tilt as they go around bends. These tilting trains can travel safely on normal track at very high speeds.

CIVIL ENGINEERING
Engineering projects provide transport with its infrastructure – the non-moving parts such as airports, tunnels, motorways, and bridges. Most projects involve earth-moving on a vast scale and millions of tonnes of concrete. Bridges can span gaps of more than 1 km (0.6 mile), while there are rail tunnels more than 50 km (30 miles) long. Huge airstrips can be built by filling shallow areas of sea with rock and rubble to create new land.

Building the Channel Tunnel between Britain and France

More people, more cars – more problems

For many people, travelling by car became essential to their way of life. But by the 1980s, more people were becoming aware that a price had to be paid for the convenience of owning a car and the freedom to travel. More traffic meant more noise, fumes, and congestion, and more countryside disappearing under concrete as new motorways were built. It has been predicted that by the year 2025 there could be more than twice as many vehicles on the world's roads. How will the Earth's atmosphere react to the pollution created by so many cars? And will the world's oil supplies be able to support such a huge volume of traffic? It seems clear that car drivers the world over will have to change their habits in the 21st century.

Rotating television camera
Satellite dish

The *Viking 1* Mars lander, 1976

A never-ending journey?

Whatever happens on Earth, out in space one thing is certain: the longest journey ever undertaken will go steadily on, as the spacecraft *Voyager 2* speeds farther and farther into the icy darkness of the Universe. *Voyager 2* left Earth in 1977 and flew past the planets Jupiter, Saturn, Uranus, and Neptune, before leaving the Solar System for ever. This robot explorer will continue its extraordinary voyage of discovery into deep space for many millions of years to come.

Mir space station, launched 1986

THE TECHNOLOGY OF TRANSPORT

ROCKET POWER

The simplest rocket is a balloon, blown up and released without closing the nozzle so that it flies around the room. By shooting out air backwards, the balloon propels itself forwards. Real rockets work in the same way, except that they blast out white-hot gas instead of air. A rocket motor burns fuel so fast that it gives thousands of times more power than any other motor of a similar size. Fuel needs oxygen to burn, so rockets carry an oxidant that allows the fuel to burn in space, where there is no natural oxygen. The Space Shuttle uses liquid hydrogen as its main fuel, with liquid oxygen as the oxidant.

Space Shuttle *Endeavour* on "Crawler", the world's largest land vehicle

JET PROPULSION

Like a rocket, a jet engine obtains its thrust by blowing out a jet of hot gas. Unlike a rocket, it gets its oxygen by using a fan to draw in air at the front. This air is forced into a combustion chamber, where it is mixed with fuel and burned to produce the blast of hot gas. Most jet engines are turbofans, with a huge propeller-like fan at the front. Powered by the engine itself, the fan draws in air for the combustion chamber, and sends some air down the outside of the engine. This "jacket" of air adds to the thrust and cuts down noise.

Front view of a turbofan engine

EXPLORING THE DEEP

While astronauts were venturing into space, other explorers were turning towards the Earth's last frontier – the ocean depths. They used diving vessels with strengthened hulls to withstand the huge pressures of the deep ocean. In 1960, Jacques Piccard and Donald Walsh reached a record depth of 11 km (7 miles) in their bathyscaphe *Trieste*. Deep-sea expeditions have also searched for mineral and oil deposits, mapped the sea-floor, and found new species of fish and other kinds of life.

Propellers

Solar-powered car

ENERGY CRISIS

By 1990, there were 400 million cars in the world. Oil supplies are dwindling, and pollution from car exhausts is damaging the atmosphere. Scientists are still searching for an alternative to the petrol-powered car. At present, solar and electric cars are little more than novelties, and fall a long way short of the performance required by most motorists.

NEW SHIPS, NEW USES

New types of ship have been built to cope with changing demand. Roll-on roll-off car ferries, with doors at both ends, were developed because people wanted to take their cars with them on holiday. In coastal waters, hovercraft and hydrofoils now provide passengers with high-speed services. Supertankers have replaced luxury liners as the new giants of the seas, carrying oil to meet the world's fuel needs.

Rudder

Hydrofoil, 1980

Crew travelled in the strengthened steel ball

Trieste bathyscaphe, 1960

Washington National Airport, Washington DC, USA

MASS AIR TRAVEL

When wide-bodied jets came into service in the 1970s, air travel became affordable for millions more people. Since then, airports have expanded rapidly to cope with the increasing flood of passengers, but they are often overwhelmed at busy periods. Like miniature towns, major airports now contain shops, restaurants, and even places of worship, with hotels located nearby.

1960

| 1960 | 1961 | | 1964 |

AIR & SPACE

1961•
HAWKER SIDDELEY P.1127 *Britain*
The P.1127 first flew in 1961. It could take off vertically and hover, and yet fly much faster than a helicopter. The Harrier jet fighter, developed from the P.1127, entered service in 1969. The swivelling joints on its jet exhausts allow thrust to be directed horizontally for high-speed flight, and downwards for take off and landing. It does not need a runway, and can stop and turn in mid-flight.

Sloping wings

Front view of Hawker Harrier GR5, 1989

Disposable fuel pod

Air intake

Swivelling nozzle on exhaust of jet engine

F-111 with wings forward

•1964 GENERAL DYNAMICS F-111 *USA*
It is difficult to design aircraft that can fly at high supersonic speeds, but also perform well at lower, subsonic speeds. General Dynamics' F-111, first flown in 1964, overcomes this problem with "swing-wings". At low-speed, the wings are swung forward, as on normal aircraft. For supersonic flight, the wings are folded back, giving a smaller wing area and a more aerodynamic "delta" shape.

F-111 with wings partially swept back

•1961 VOSTOK 1 *USSR*
The USSR startled the world on 12 April, 1961, when cosmonaut Yuri Gagarin became the first person in space. In his *Vostok 1* spacecraft, he made a single orbit of the Earth on a journey lasting 108 minutes. On his return to Earth, Gagarin ejected from the spacecraft at a height of 7,000 m (23,000 ft), and landed safely by parachute.

Vostok 1, 1961

LAND

The large sail, like that of a modern windsurfer, can be moved from side to side to catch the wind.

The Mini's great cornering ability was the result of its low centre of gravity and wheels placed at the extreme corners of the car.

Spotlamp for night rallying

NSU Spyder, 1964

24PK

Steering oar

Austin Mini-Cooper S, 1963

•1963
NSU SPYDER *Germany*
Germany's NSU Spyder was the first car to have a new type of engine called a Wankel engine. This small, lightweight, yet powerful engine used a triangular "piston" rotating in an oval chamber.

•1963
AUSTIN MINI-COOPER *Britain*
The Austin Mini-Cooper was a high-performance version of Britain's Mini-Minor, which was first produced in 1958. The Mini was the first front-wheel-drive car to have its engine and gearbox mounted "transversely", or parallel to the axle. Most family cars today have this layout.

•1964
BULLET TRAIN *Japan*
Japan's electric Shinkansen, or "new high-speed railway", opened between Tokyo and Osaka in 1964. Its 12-car "bullet trains" were the world's fastest, capable of 210 kph (130 mph). The passengers enjoyed smooth travelling, good sound insulation, and comfortable, open-plan carriages with aircraft-style seats. *See* TGV 1981.

Bullet train passing Mt. Fuji

WATER

The "daggerboard" is pushed down at sea to stop the raft from drifting sideways.

France, 1962

Jangada, 1960

The tapered raft is made of logs lashed or pinned together.

c.1960
JANGADA *Brazil*
Long before windsurfing became a leisure craze, Brazilian aces were skimming across the sea on "jangadas". These traditional rafts are still used for fishing up to 50 km (30 miles) off the east coast of Brazil. Similar craft have been used in South America for at least 400 years. *See* WINDSURFER 1977.

Roller for moving raft down beach into sea

Fishermen strap themselves to the deck when they sleep, so they are not washed overboard.

•1962 FRANCE *France*
At 301 m (1,035 ft), the 66,000-tonne *France* was the longest ship in the world. It was designed to carry 2,000 passengers or more between Europe and America. But the luxury transatlantic liners gradually lost more and more customers to jet airliners. *France* was later renamed *Norway*, and started a new life as a cruise ship.

•1963 LIGHTSHIP *Britain*
Lightships are unpowered vessels that are towed out to sea and moored over offshore obstructions such as sandbanks. A diesel generator provides electricity for the warning light, and supplies the crew's needs. Some modern lightships are automatic, controlled by radio signals from the shore.

Model of Kentish Knock lightship, 1963

KENTISH KNOCK

MILESTONES

1960–1964

•**1960** The world's airlines now carry 100 million passengers a year.
•**1960** *Triton*, the US Navy's nuclear submarine, goes around the world in 85 days without surfacing.
•**1961** The Hawker P.1127 "jump-jet" makes its first successful vertical take-off and landing.
•**1961** Cosmonaut Yuri Gagarin from the USSR becomes the first person in space in *Vostok 1*.
•**1961** Alan B. Shepard becomes the first American in space when he makes a 15-minute sub-orbital flight.

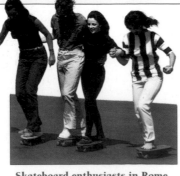
Skateboard enthusiasts in Rome, Italy, early 1960s

•**1961** US President John F. Kennedy announces that his country will send astronauts to the Moon before 1970.
•**1962** John H. Glenn becomes the first American in orbit aboard *Friendship 7*.
•**1962** In England, Alex Moulton patents a new bicycle design with much smaller wheels than normal bicycles.
•**1963** Improvements in the design of boards mean that more people are taking up skateboarding.
•**1963** Germany's NSU Spyder is the first car to have a Wankel engine.
•**1963** Valentina Tereshkova of the USSR is the first woman in space.

Valentina Tereshkova, first woman in space, 1963

•**1964** "Bullet trains" – the world's fastest – enter service in Japan.
•**1964** Jerrie Mock of the USA becomes the first woman to fly solo around the world.
•**1964** Englishman Donald Campbell pushes the world land speed record up to 648 kph (403 mph) in his car *Bluebird II*, and drives a speedboat at 445 kph (276 mph).
•**1964** Three Soviet astronauts orbit the Earth 17 times in *Voskhod 1*.
•**1964** America's Lockheed SR-71A Blackbird flies at three times the speed of sound. *See* MILESTONES 1976.

1966   1967   1968   1969

The tip of the Command Module contains parachutes and airbags for a safe "splashdown" at sea.

Small engines to help control the LEM in flight

The legs have rounded feet to stop them from sinking into the Moon dust.

The LEM has four "spider" legs that fold up in flight.

Model of Apollo Lunar Excursion Module (LEM)

The module is scorched as it re-enters the Earth's atmosphere.

Apollo Command Module

1969•
APOLLO 11 SPACE MISSION *USA*
A three-stage Saturn V rocket launched the *Apollo 11* spacecraft that made the first Moon landing on 20 July, 1969. Each stage was jettisoned after burning up its fuel. The powerful first stage lifted the 2,902-tonne rocket from the Earth's surface to a height of 58 km (36 miles) in only 2.5 minutes. After the third stage had fired, *Apollo 11* had enough momentum to coast across to the Moon. The Command and Service Modules stayed in orbit, while two crew members descended to the Moon in the Lunar Excursion Module (LEM). When they rejoined their fellow astronaut, the LEM was abandoned and *Apollo 11* returned to Earth. The astronauts made a safe landing at sea in the Command Module.

Launch escape tower

Command Module

Service Module

LEM

Saturn V rocket used for Apollo Moon missions

Third stage

•1965
MACLAREN BUGGY
Britain
Former engineer and designer Owen Maclaren developed a revolutionary push chair or "buggy" for carrying babies and children. He used his specialized knowledge of materials and structures to make his lightweight buggy as strong as possible. It could be folded up and put away or carried like an umbrella when not in use.

Maclaren buggy, 1965

Seat belt

1967-8•
HONDA CB750 *Japan*
Until the mid-1960s, most motorcycles had single- or twin-cylinder engines. A few racing machines used multi-cylinder engines, including the four-cylinder Honda ridden by Englishman Mike Hailwood in 1967. Within months, Honda had incorporated this engine into the CB750, which went on sale in 1968. With its amazing acceleration and top speed of 190 kph, (120 mph), the CB750 started a craze for "superbikes". It was smooth running, reliable, quiet, and did not leak oil.

Oil tank

Petrol tank

Instruments

Honda CB750, 1969

Telescopic forks

Disc brakes

Four-cylinder engine

Double exhausts on each side of wheel

USA

Second stage

Seatask model, 1965

Chamber at normal air pressure

•1965 *SEATASK* DIVING BELL *Britain*
Seatask was one of the earliest diving bells used to take divers into deep water to carry out oil-exploration work. Divers leave the bell once the bottom chamber has been pressurized to the external water pressure. When they re-enter the chamber, it is sealed and the bell is raised to the surface. At the surface, the chamber is slowly depressurized to normal air pressure. This prevents the divers suffering from the "bends", which can be fatal.

•1968 SR-N4 HOVERCRAFT *Britain*
The SR-N4 is the world's largest hovercraft. Able to do 65 knots (120 kph/75 mph) in calm water, it is faster than conventional passenger and car ferries. Fans under a flexible rubber "skirt" raise the craft above the water, and propellers on top drive it forward. At its destination, the SR-N4 simply glides up a ramp onto dry land. See HOVERCRAFT 1955, and *HISHO* HOVERCRAFT 1994.

SR-N4 hovercraft, 1968

Stacked containers

1969•
CONTAINER SHIP *Britain*
With the development of container ships such as *Encounter Bay* in the 1960s, loss or damage to cargo in rough seas became a thing of the past. Most cargo carried by ships is now sealed in standard-sized containers that are secured by guide rails and racks on the ship. On land, the containers fit onto specially built trucks or railway wagons.

Decompression chamber

Model of *Encounter Bay* container ship, 1969

First stage

USA

1965–1969

Entry hatch

•**1965** Much sea cargo is now carried in standard pre-packed containers aboard specially designed "container ships".
•**1965** In the USA, Craig Breedlove sets a land speed record of 967 kph (601 mph) in his jet-propelled car *Spirit of America*.
•**1965** At London's Heathrow airport, a Hawker Siddeley Trident airliner makes the first automatic landing by a scheduled airline flight.
•**1966** Controversy over an American book titled *Unsafe at Any Speed* makes car manufacturers in the USA and elsewhere conscious of the need to build safer cars.

First automatic landing, by scheduled airline flight, 1965

•**1967** The Transit navigation system is in commercial use. It allows land, sea, and air travellers to find their location by receiving radio waves from satellites.
•**1967** The first Saturn V rocket – the type that will eventually take people to the Moon –makes a successful test flight.
•**1968** The USA introduces new laws to reduce vehicle exhaust fumes.
•**1968** The Soviet Tupolev Tu-144 is the first supersonic airliner to fly. It never goes into full service, and will crash at the Paris Air show in 1973.
•**1968** The SR-N4 hovercraft enters service between England and France.

•**1969** American astronauts Eugene Cernan, John Young, and Thomas Stafford become the fastest humans ever, when their *Apollo 10* spacecraft reaches 39,897 kph (24,791 mph).
•**1969** The USA's *Apollo 11* astronauts Neil Armstrong and "Buzz Aldrin" become the first people to visit another world when they land on the Moon.
•**1969** The Anglo-French supersonic airliner Concorde flies for the first time. It begins a seven-year programme of rigorous testing. See CONCORDE 1976.
•**1969** The Boeing 747 makes its first flight. See BOEING 747 1970.

1970

AIR & SPACE

•1970 BOEING 747 *USA*
The Boeing 747 "Jumbo" entered service in 1970. It is the world's largest passenger aircraft, weighing about 300 tonnes, and with room for more than 300 passengers. During the 1960s, there were fears it would be unsafe to carry so many people in one aircraft. Such fears were quickly dispelled by the success of the 747, which has proved reliable, safe, and economical.

Boeing 747, 1970

1973•
BELL JETRANGER *USA*
The Bell JetRanger was the result of an unsuccessful military project. The Bell company of Texas, USA, had failed to win orders for a gas-turbine powered observation helicopter, and in 1965 adapted their design for the civilian market. The stylish JetRanger became hugely popular with business people who wanted to travel in comfort and make a good impression when they arrived for business meetings. The JetRanger's performance improved so much during the 1970s that military interest was rekindled, and large numbers were bought by armed forces throughout the world.

Bell JetRanger, 1973

•1973 *SKYLAB* *USA*
Skylab was the first purpose-built space laboratory. Between 1973 and 1974, three teams of astronauts lived there for a total of 171 days, studying space medicine and technology, and the Earth's resources. *Skylab* was designed to stay in space until 1983, but gradually lost height and broke up in the Earth's atmosphere in 1979.

Antenna
Control panel
Television camera

Lunar Rover, 1971

Skylab, **1973**

LAND

•1970
INDIAN PACIFIC *Australia*
Australia's streamlined, stainless-steel Indian Pacific train was introduced between Sydney and Perth in 1970. This luxurious air-conditioned train covers the coast-to-coast route in just under 3 days. Passengers are offered sleeping accommodation with private showers and toilets. Other facilities include a cocktail lounge, a drawing-room, and a music room with piano.

The Indian Pacific

•1971
LUNAR ROVER *USA*
On the 1971 *Apollo 15* mission, the astronauts took with them a collapsible buggy, called the "Lunar Rover", for venturing farther afield from the landing site. On Earth, the battery-powered buggy weighed 210 kg (463 lb), but on the Moon its weight was only 35 kg (77 lb). Its wire-mesh tyres would have collapsed on Earth under the weight. The buggy – like others from later missions – was left on the Moon, where it remains to this day.

Wire-mesh wheel

•1973
SPORTS CARS *USA/Japan*
In the 1970s, American and Japanese car manufacturers began to challenge the European dominance of the sports car market. A good example of the new generation of American sports cars was the Pontiac Firebird Trans-Am. Beneath its strikingly decorated bonnet lay a powerful 224-kW (300-hp) engine. In Japan, Datsun took up the challenge with its Z-series sports coupé. The 240 Z, and its larger-engined successor the 280 Z, became the world's best-selling sports cars.

Pontiac Firebird Trans-Am, 1973

Datsun 240 Z, 1973

Tail fin
Main turbine
Conning tower
Periscope
Torpedoes fired from tubes in bow

WATER

1971•
FRIGATE *Britain*
A frigate is a small, general-purpose warship that can perform a variety of roles, such as waging anti-submarine warfare or protecting merchant shipping. Unlike earlier warships, modern frigates have few guns, but their guided missiles and electronic warfare systems more than make up for this.

Radar mast
Helicopter

Model of British Type 21 class frigate, 1971

Model of hunter-killer submarine, 1974

Reactor space
Torpedo compartment

1973•
LIQUEFIED-GAS TANKER *Norway*
All gases turn to liquid if they are cooled and pressurized enough. Fuel gases such as methane, propane, and butane occupy only a tiny fraction of their normal volume when liquefied, making it possible to transport them in tankers. The liquid gas is stored under pressure in refrigerated spherical tanks, the tops of which can be seen projecting above the deck level.

•1974 NUCLEAR SUBMARINE
The largest nuclear submarines are literally underwater launch-pads for ballistic missiles. There are also smaller vessels, called "hunter-killer" submarines, that carry torpedoes rather than missiles. In wartime, hunter-killers prowl the oceans silently, preying on enemy ships. The nuclear reactor powers the submarine's turbines, and produces electricity and fresh water for the crew.

Model of *Norman Lady* liquefied-gas tanker, 1973

Gun turret

Variable pitch propeller
Torpedo tube
Stabilizer
Sonar bulge
Missile launcher

MILESTONES

•**1970s** Hydrofoils (fast boats with hulls that lift out of the water on "wings") are becoming more common on rivers and lakes, particularly in the Soviet Union.
•**1970** The new 3,960-km (2,460-mile) Trans-Australia Railway opens, linking Sydney and Perth.
•**1970** Two Sikorsky HH-53C helicopters are the first to fly the Pacific non-stop, refuelling in flight.

•**1970** An explosion in *Apollo 13* puts at risk the lives of three American astronauts on their way to the Moon. By improvization, they survive for four days, returning safely to Earth.
•**1970** Three Soviet cosmonauts spend 24 days in *Salyut 1*, the first space station to orbit the Earth. All three die as they prepare to return to Earth, because of a malfunction aboard their spacecraft.

•**1971** American astronauts tour the Moon in a lightweight electric car called the "Lunar Rover".
•**1972** Astronauts say goodbye to the Moon at the end of the *Apollo 17* mission. No one else will visit the Earth's satellite in the 20th century.
•**1973** Petrol costs soar after Middle Eastern countries raise oil prices. As a result, smaller, more efficient cars start to become more popular.

Queuing during the petrol crisis of 1973

•**1973** *Skylab*, an orbiting space station, is launched from the USA.
•**1973** A suspension bridge opens across the Bosporus at Istanbul, Turkey, linking Europe and Asia.
•**1974** Only 45,000 people die in road accidents in the USA this year, compared with 54,000 in 1973. The fall is partly the result of a new 88 kph (55 mph) speed limit.
•**1974** Oil is now transported around the world in huge ships called "supertankers".

1975

1975	1976	1977	1978	1979

•1976 CONCORDE *Britain/France*
Developed by the British Aircraft Corporation and Aérospatiale of France, Concorde entered service in 1976. This supersonic airliner can cross the Atlantic Ocean in as little as 3 hours, with a cruising speed of 2,338 kph (1,453 mph). The "droop nose" is lowered during take-off and landing to give a better view out of the cockpit. Its noisy turbojet engines burn twice as much fuel as the quieter turbofans of ordinary airliners. Aircraft moving at supersonic speeds create shock waves that are heard on the ground as a loud "boom". For this reason, Concorde has to travel at subsonic speeds over inhabited areas.

Tail fin

Model of Concorde (front view)

Engine air intake

Dassault-Breguet Mystère-Falcon 50, 1979

•1979 BUSINESS JET *France*
The Dassault-Breguet Mystère-Falcon 50 started production in 1979, and the fifth to be built was chosen as the French President's private aircraft. Business jets such as the Falcon carry busy executives quickly (if expensively) between commercial centres. Tables allow the Falcon's passengers to work as they travel.

Tail rudder

Emergency door

Cutaway of Concorde, 1976

Hang-glider c.1975

•1975 HANG-GLIDER
Hang-gliding was well established by the mid-1970s. A hang-glider is really just a huge wing with a harness and framework below to hold the pilot. To launch the glider, the pilot simply runs downhill into the wind. Like a normal glider, a hang-glider soars on currents of rising air. The pilot shifts his or her body to control the flight. A hang-glider can be dismantled easily and carried on a car roof. See **GLIDER 1895**.

Fuel tanks in wings

Engine exhaust

Seats for crew
Retractable visor
Weather radar
Passenger seating
Wings are covered by a "skin" of metal panels
Passenger door
High-pressure tyres
Four-wheel bogie
Rolls-Royce Olympus Mark 610 turbojet engine

c.1975 ARTICULATED FREIGHT TRUCK *USA*
Road surfaces are easily damaged by wheels carrying heavy loads, so freight trucks use several axles to reduce the weight carried by individual wheels. This results in longer vehicles that need to be articulated – that is, with a front tractor unit and a trailer behind, connected by a swivelling joint. The rapid growth of container traffic in the mid-1970s resulted in many more of these monsters, which had to be large enough to accommodate standard 12-m (40-ft) sea containers. See **CONTAINER SHIP 1969**.

Refrigerated trailer unit

Articulated freight truck, USA, mid-1970s

"Soft-top" hood is folded back in fine weather

Volkswagen Beetle, 1979

•1979 VOLKSWAGEN "BEETLE" *Germany*
By the early 1970s, more Volkswagen "Beetles" had been made than any other car in history. In 1977, car number 16,255,500 left the factory, and the company decided to stop production in Germany. But European demand remained so high that Beetles made under licence in Central and South America were imported into Europe in the late 1970s and early 1980s.

1975• BOEING JETFOIL *USA*
A jetfoil is a hydrofoil driven by a jet of water pumped out of the back. Underwater "wings" on long struts project from the base of the hull. As speed increases, the wings produce lift, and the hull rises clear of the water. This eliminates the drag of water past the hull, allowing speeds of 43 knots (80 kph/50 mph).

A jetfoil rides the waves on its underwater wings

•1977 WINDSURFER *USA*
Californian Hoyle Schweitzer took out the first patent on a windsurfer in 1968, but controversy surrounds the date of the earliest windsurfer, with one claim dating back to 1958. A windsurfer is basically a surfboard with a movable triangular sail. Windsurfing grew rapidly as a sport in the late 1970s and early 1980s, with competitions such as wave jumping and distance racing. In 1984, it became part of the Olympic Games.

Windsurfer, 1977

•1978 SUPERTANKER
Much of the world's oil is carried in Ultra-Large Crude Carriers (ULCCs) or "supertankers". Weighing nearly 500,000 tonnes, they are 450 m (1,475 ft) long and dwarf all other ships on the sea. In fact, they are so big that they take several kilometres to turn or stop. When fully laden, they sit alarmingly low in the water, with waves crashing over the deck – but they are really very stable. Oil is lighter than water, and this makes the ships very buoyant.

Supertanker, 1978

•**1975** Commercial airliners now use "inertial navigation", a system that uses an on-board computer to work out the exact position of an aircraft at all times, without reference to anything outside the aircraft.
•**1975** Hijackings and terrorist attacks mean that airports and airlines have to tighten their security operations.
•**1975** The world's first regular jetfoil service starts in Hong Kong.
•**1975** A new law in the USA aims to save petrol by requiring all new cars to do at least 11.7 km to the litre (27.5 miles to the gallon) by 1985.

•**1976** Simultaneous take-offs by Concorde aircraft in Britain and France inaugurate the first supersonic passenger services.
•**1976** A world air speed record of 3,530 kph (2,193 mph) is set by a Lockheed SR-71A Blackbird over California, USA.
•**1976** A 1,859-km (1,155-mile) railway opens between Tanzania and Zambia in Africa.
•**1976** Two American Viking robot spacecraft land on Mars. They search for signs of life on the planet, but do not find any.

Robot car manufacturing like this began in the 1970s

•**1977** Computer-controlled robots are now used to make cars, particularly in Japan, where 7,000 such robots are at work.
•**1978** In Utah, USA, *Lightning Bolt*, a twin-engined motorcycle, achieves a motorcycle speed record of 513 kph (319 mph).
•**1978** A solar-powered car runs at 13 kph (8 mph) in England.

•**1978** Australian Kenneth Warby achieves a world water speed record of 278 knots (514 kph/320 mph) in his boat *Spirit of Australia*.

•**1979** A model "maglev" (magnetic levitation) train is tested to a speed of 515 kph (320 mph) in Japan. Maglev trains do not touch their rails, but float just above them by means of strong magnetic forces.
•**1979** A pedal-powered aircraft, *Gossamer Albatross*, is flown from England to France by American racing cyclist Bryan Allen.

1980

1980   1981   1983   1984

AIR & SPACE

Liquid fuel tank

Solid fuel rocket booster

Space shuttle orbiter

Space Shuttle

•1981
SPACE SHUTTLE *USA*
In 1981, the Space Shuttle *Columbia* became the first re-usable space vehicle. Until then, only the Command Module of a spacecraft returned to Earth – the rest was left in space. This was wasteful, and meant that tasks such as repairing orbiting satellites were impossible. The Shuttle's boosters and fuel tanks fall away after take-off, and its own engines take it into space. The wings begin to work as the Shuttle re-enters the atmosphere, allowing it to glide to a landing strip, where it touches down like a normal aircraft.

Columbia **glides to Earth, 1981**

•1983
PITTS SPECIAL S-2S *USA*
Thrilling displays from the tiny Pitts Special are always popular at airshows. An American, Curtis Pitts, built the first one in 1944 for aerobatic contests. The S-2S version has a mighty 194-kW (260-hp) engine crammed into its long nose. The wings are the same shape on the top and bottom, enabling the aircraft to fly just as well upside-down as it does the right way up.

Astronaut with MMU

Pitts Special S-2S, 1983

G-PITZ

•1984 JETPACK *USA*
In 1984, Space Shuttle astronaut Bruce McCandless went for an untethered ride in space with a jetpack called a Manned Manoeuvring Unit (MMU) strapped to the back of his space suit. The MMU is propelled by 24 tiny jets of nitrogen gas, fed from two high-pressure cylinders. The jets are controlled by a joystick, allowing the astronaut to move freely.

•1984
MAGLEV TRAIN *Germany*
Magnetic levitation trains float above their track, supported by magnetic fields. Driven by linear motors, which have no moving parts, "maglev" passenger trains of the future will ride smoothly, efficiently, and quietly at up to 700 kph (435 mph). Germany's Transrapid project began in 1984, aiming to develop a high-speed, intercity maglev train that would travel on a raised track. Working prototypes have also been built in Japan.

LAND

•1981 TGV *France*
French Railways' prestigious "Trains à Grande Vitesse" (high-speed trains) first went into service between Paris and Lyons in 1981. The trains are made up of eight or nine carriages with a locomotive at each end. On some routes, TGVs run at up to 300 kph (186 mph). TGVs can only reach such speeds on specially built, or "dedicated", track with steeply banked curves. They cannot run at full speed on ordinary track.

French Railways' TGV train, introduced 1981

Transrapid 06 maglev train

Computers furl and unfurl sails automatically

Sail of taut canvas over steel frame

Modern yachts have masts made of strong, lightweight metal alloys, and sails woven from synthetic materials.

Model of *Shin Aitoku Maru*, 1980

Model of *Maiden* yacht, 1981

Osel Duplus submersible, 1983

Power cable

Thruster

Observation window

Manipulator arm

Grabber

WATER

•1980
SAIL-ASSISTED SHIP *Japan*
Early steamships carried sails because the engines were not powerful or reliable enough. Inspired by high fuel costs, sail-assisted ships made a comeback in the 1980s. The Japanese tanker *Shin Aitoku Maru*'s two sails lower fuel consumption by 10 per cent. They also give the ship a smoother ride in rough seas. When under sail, computers reduce the power from the main diesel engine accordingly.

•1981 RACING YACHT *Britain*
The design of ocean racing yachts is a compromise between the need to reduce weight above the waterline for maximum speed, and yet have sufficient weight low down to counteract the tilting force of the tall sails. These yachts must be able to withstand rough seas. Consequently, they are often built using unusual techniques and materials. *Maiden*, for example, had a hull made entirely of aluminium.

•1983 SUBMERSIBLE *Britain*
Many tasks once carried out by deep-sea divers are now done by underwater submersibles. The vessel above carries one pilot, who lies inside on his or her stomach. The pilot breathes air at normal pressure, so there is no risk of the bends. The grabber and arms are used to handle equipment. *See SEATASK DIVING BELL, 1965.*

1980–1984

Voyager 2 robot spacecraft

Communications antenna

Radioactive power source

MILESTONES

•1980 Seven million motorcycles will be built in the world this year, more than 90 per cent of them in Japan.
•1980 The 16-km (10-mile) long St. Gotthard road tunnel under the Alps opens to traffic.
•1980 The US Navy's SES-100B hovercraft reaches a record speed of 92 knots (170 kph/106 mph).
•1981 There are 330 million cars in the world, 80 per cent of them in Japan, Europe, and North America. Japan now makes more new cars each year than the USA.

•1981 The Space Shuttle *Columbia* makes its first successful orbital flight.
•1981 The American robot spacecraft *Voyager 2* passes within 101,000 km (63,000 miles) of Saturn. Launched in 1977, *Voyager 2* has also flown close to Jupiter, and will visit Uranus (1986) and Neptune (1989) before leaving the Solar System for ever.
•1981 A suspension bridge opens over the Humber Estuary in England with a central span of 1,410 m (4,625 ft) – the world's longest.

Humber Bridge, opened 1981

•1981 In France, the high-speed electric TGV train goes into service.
•1982 The Japanese Datsun 280 ZX car has an electronic warning voice that speaks to the driver if anything goes wrong.

•1983 Englishman Richard Noble sets a land speed record of 1,019 kph (633 mph) in the jet-powered *Thrust 2*.
•1983 Driverless trains run on the new underground railway in Lille, France.
•1983 Because of pollution worries, car drivers start to use unleaded fuel.
•1984 An American astronaut flies freely in space using a jetpack.
•1984 Three Soviet cosmonauts spend a record 238 days in space in the orbiting station *Salyut 7*.
•1984 New safety rules in the USA insist that all new cars must have air bags and automatic seat belts by 1990.

1985

1985   1986   1987

**Northrop B-2
stealth bomber,
1989**

Air intake

*Wing
containing
fuel tanks*

•1986 RUTAN VOYAGER *USA*
In 1986, the ultra-lightweight *Voyager* made a 40,000-km (25,000-mile) round-the-world flight without refuelling. *Voyager* was piloted by Dick Rutan and Jeana Yeager, who took turns at the controls in a cramped cockpit only 62 cm (24 in) wide. *Voyager* was designed by Dick's brother Burt, with the aim of minimizing its weight and wind resistance, and enabling it to carry as much fuel as possible.

Rutan Voyager, 1986

•1986 BEECH STARSHIP *USA*
The Beech Aircraft Corporation's 11-seater Starship made headlines for its extensive use of lightweight, plastic-based "composite" materials. This business aircraft has two "pusher" propellers at the back of the aircraft. The Starship also has wing-tip extensions called "winglets", which improve the wings' performance and save fuel. Like *Voyager*, the Starship was designed by Burt Rutan.

**Beech
Starship,
1986**

•1989 STEALTH BOMBER *USA*
The Northrop B-2, known as the "stealth bomber", flew for the first time in 1989. The B-2's role is to make high-speed dashes into enemy territory and deliver a 23-tonne bomb load without being detected. This tail-less aircraft, with its jagged shape and concealed engine intakes, is designed to be "invisible" to enemy radar. Its non-reflective coating and extensive use of non-metallic composite materials help to minimize the reflection of radar signals.

*Illuminated
"for hire" sign*   *Radio aerial*

**London
"black cab"**

*Hood to shelter
passengers*

**Cycle-
rickshaw,
Bangladesh**

*Pedals drive a
chain that turns
the rear axle.*

c.1985 CITY TAXIS
Taxis – vehicles for hire – are an important part of the transport system in cities today. Some taxis have a distinctive look that has become associated with a particular city or part of the world. London's "black cabs", for example, have looked virtually the same since 1958. And visitors to New York expect to see the famous yellow taxis. But not all taxis are motor-driven. The cycle-rickshaw is a pedal-powered version of earlier ones pulled by people or horses. This energy-efficient "taxi" is typical of many cities in Asia.
See JINRIKISHA 1892.

**New York
yellow taxi**

•1987 MOUNTAIN CABLE CAR
New Zealand
In the 19th century, cable cars were used in the Swiss and Austrian Alps to allow visitors to enjoy the fine views. In 1987, new cars were installed on the Austrian-designed system at Bob's Peak in New Zealand. The 4-seater cars hang from a cable 35 mm (1.5 in) thick, and travel 450 m (1,476 ft) to the summit. Cars coming down counterbalance those going up, making the system safer and reducing the power needed to pull the cars.

**Cable car at Bob's Peak,
New Zealand**

•1989 MOUNTAIN BIKE *Canada*
The first all-terrain "mountain bike" was made by Americans Charles Kelly and Gary Fisher in 1981. By the late 1980s, mountain bikes had become popular throughout the world. The robust, lightweight frames, straight handlebars, thick tyres, and multiple gears make them ideal both for off-road use and city-centre cycling.

**Rocky
Mountain
"Experience",
1989**   *Chunky
tyres*

*The hull has a surface
layer of stainless
steel to protect it
in icy water.*

**Otso
icebreaker,
1986**

•1986 ICEBREAKER *Finland*
Icebreakers are vital for keeping seaways open in freezing Arctic waters. Early icebreakers had propellers at the bows, as well as at the stern, to power through the ice. Instead of bow propellers, Finland's *Otso* icebreaker uses high-pressure air bubbling out of the bow under the waterline. This acts rather like a lubricant, helping the hull to slide more easily through the thick mixture of broken ice and cold water.

OTSO

RoRo ferry

•1988 ROLL-ON ROLL-OFF FERRY *Britain*
Roll-on Roll-off (RoRo) car ferries have doors at the bows and the stern, so that cars can be driven aboard, parked, and driven off without lengthy manoeuvring or handling by cranes. Most of these ships have side and bow thrusters (extra propellers), allowing them to dock in busy ports without using tugs.

•1989 POWERBOAT *Britain*
Offshore powerboat racing became a regular spectacle in the 1980s. Driven by engines similar to those used in racing cars, powerboats leap off wave-crests at high speed. The pilots need great skill and quick reflexes to avoid a rough landing that could not only damage the boat, but also cause them serious injury – falling into the sea at high speed can feel like hitting a brick wall.

**Pachanga 27
powerboat, 1989**

•1985 Chicago's O'Hare airport in the USA is the world's busiest, with 44,000,000 passengers and 700,000 flights a year.
•1985 NASA, the American space agency, starts to plan a permanently orbiting space station, but it will only ever be built if the US government agrees to provide massive funding.
•1986 After a 9-day flight, America's *Voyager* aircraft is the first to fly around the world without refuelling.
•1986 The European *Giotto* spacecraft flies within 600 km (370 miles) of the nucleus of Halley's Comet.

•1986 After ten successful flights in the past year, the US Space Shuttle programme is halted when the Space Shuttle *Challenger* explodes in mid-air, killing all seven crew members.
•1986 Two Soviet cosmonauts spend 4 months in space, visiting the old *Salyut* 7 and the new *Mir* orbiting space stations.
•1986 Engineers in California, USA, consider plans for automatic motorways, on which computers will control the spacing of cars and apply brakes when necessary.

•1988 The new 500-seater Boeing 747-400 Advanced Superjet has a range of 13,000 km (8,000 miles).
•1988 Work starts on Japan's Akashi suspension bridge. Its 2-km (1.2-mile) central span will be the world's longest.
•1988 In Japan, the world's longest rail tunnel is completed. The 54-km (33-mile) Seikan tunnel links the islands of Honshu and Hokkaido.
•1988 The most powerful diesel engines ever built, capable of 43 MW (58,000 hp), are being installed in new container ships.

**A view down the Seikan tunnel in
Japan, completed in 1988**

•1988 The Soviet space shuttle orbiter *Buran* makes its only flight.
•1988 In the USA, a solar-powered vehicle called the *Sunraycer* reaches a speed of 78 kph (49 mph).
•1989 The tanker *Exxon Valdez* spills 32,000 tonnes of oil after running aground in the Gulf of Alaska, USA. Cleaning up will cost more than 1 billion dollars.
•1989 The American Northrop B-2 stealth bomber makes its first flight.
•1989 A 33-m (110-ft) powerboat called *Gentry Eagle* crosses the Atlantic in 2 days and 14 hours.

1990

AIR & SPACE

•1990 MICROLIGHT *Britain*
The first microlights were made simply by fitting an engine and a propeller to a hang-glider. But the frames of ordinary hang-gliders were not really strong enough to bear the extra weight. A modern microlight is much safer, with a strong, specially designed frame and a streamlined fibreglass "tricycle" slung beneath to carry the pilot. The wheels enable it to take off and land like a normal aircraft. "Ultralights" are similar, but have rigid wings.

The rotor blades are made of the latest composite materials.

Westland-Agusta EH-101, 1994

The wingspan is 10.3 m (34 ft).

G-0101

HELILINER

Undercarriage is retracted during flight

•1994 WESTLAND-AGUSTA EH-101 *Britain/Italy*
The EH-101 is a multi-purpose helicopter that can be used for passenger transport, air-sea rescue, and military roles. The unusual shape of the rotor blades reduces fuel consumption. In the past, helicopter travel was noisy and unpleasant, but the EH-101 uses ingenious technology to keep vibration, and hence noise, to an absolute minimum. It also minimizes "wear and tear" on the airframe.

Microlight, 1990

Propeller
Engine
Hand-grip
Pilot sits in wheeled tricycle
Wing of light, woven fabric over metal frame
The heavy "hatchback" door has springy struts that help to lift it and keep it open.

LAND

•1990 ELEVATING WHEELCHAIR *Britain*
The Mangar Freestyle was the world's first compact elevating powered wheelchair. It has a top speed of 6.5 kph (4 mph), and can travel for 16 km (10 miles) before its batteries need recharging. The seat is raised by pressurized air in the bellows, allowing the user to reach objects far beyond the range of normal wheelchairs.

Lifting bellows
Electric motor

Mangar Freestyle wheelchair, 1990

Mazda 323, 1992

•1992 FAMILY CAR *Japan*
Sports cars and off-road vehicles may be glamorous, but the most important type of car today is the family car. Many families with small children opt for a three- or five-door "hatchback" car, such as Japan's Mazda 323. There is room in the back for one or two children, and plenty of storage space. These cars use a "transverse" engine and front-wheel drive like the original Mini (*see* **AUSTIN MINI-COOPER 1963**), but they are faster, more comfortable and more efficient.

•1993 TRIUMPH TROPHY 1200 *Britain*
After 1960, competition from superior Japanese motorcycles caused many European factories to close down. But Europe's surviving manufacturers are now making a comeback. In the early 1990s, these rejuvenated companies launched some up-to-the-minute models, such as the Triumph Trophy 1200, that were among the market's best.

Triumph Trophy 1200, 1993

WATER

•1990 WAVE-PIERCING CATAMARAN *Australia*
Traditional car and passenger ferries are slowly being replaced by wave-piercing catamarans. These vessels, pioneered by Australia's InCat company, do not ride the waves but cut right through them. They are faster, and pitch and roll less than ordinary ferries. Powered by water jets, the catamarans have a top speed of 42 knots (78 kph/48 mph).

SeaCat
SeaCat

Front and side views of 74-m (243-ft) wave-piercing catamaran

The MHD boat *Yamoto 1* undergoing trials in 1992

•1992 YAMOTO 1 *Japan*
The propulsion system of the revolutionary *Yamoto 1* has no moving parts. Motors and propellers have been eliminated by applying the magneto-hydrodynamic (MHD) principle. When a strong electric current is passed across a tube of water surrounded by powerful magnets, the water is forced through the tube. If the tube is placed beneath the waterline, the flow of water through the tube can be used to propel a boat forward. However, there are fears that passing electric currents through sea water may damage the marine environment.

1994• HISHO HOVERCRAFT *Japan*
Hovercraft development stalled after the 1970s, but now shipbuilders in Japan aim to build huge, fast, cargo-carrying craft by the year 2000. *Hisho*, the forerunner of these craft, was launched in 1994. It can carry 200 tonnes of cargo for 900 km (560 miles) at up to 54 knots (100 kph/62 mph), in rough seas once impassable to hovercraft.

Hisho, launched 1994

MILESTONES

•**1990** In the USA, General Motors shows off its battery-powered Impact car, which can travel 190 km (120 miles) at 88 kph (55 mph) before recharging.
•**1990** A large Australian-built wave-piercing catamaran (twin-hulled boat) crosses the Atlantic in 3 days and 8.5 hours.
•**1990** A French TGV train achieves a record speed of 515 kph (320 mph).
•**1990** The city of Los Angeles, USA, where 3 million people go to work daily by car, finally opens a commuter rail system.

•**1991** Work on a commercial "maglev" railway starts in Florida, USA.
•**1992** The Japanese *Yamoto 1* is the first ship to be propelled by magnetic forces.
•**1992** Japan is now the world's leading shipbuilding country.
•**1993** Engineers in Europe and America develop ideas for a successor to Concorde.
•**1993** Russia and America agree to work on a permanent orbiting space station.

Impact electric car, 1990

•**1993** In preparation for possible future exploration of Mars, an eight-legged robot called *Dante* walks into the mouth of an active volcano in Antarctica.
•**1993** New laws in California, USA, say that 10 per cent of cars sold there after 2003 must be emission-free.
•**1993** The robot space probe *Pioneer 10*, launched from the USA in 1972, is now 8 billion kilometres (5 billion miles) from Earth.
1994 The world's largest hovercraft, *Hisho* (meaning "Flight"), is launched.

Channel Tunnel train, 1994

•**1994** The rail link between England and France through the 50-km (30-mile) Channel Tunnel officially opens.
•**1994** Cable-stayed bridges (supported by slanting cables attached to a single tower) are coming into use.
•**1994** Work begins on a scheme to create an artificial island in Hong Kong harbour, on which the world's biggest airport will be built.
•**1994** A solar-powered car, *Aurora Q1*, crosses Australia in 8 days, averaging 50 kph (30 mph).

Future trends

Design for a future supersonic airliner

SUPERSONIC AIRLINERS

To meet the demand for rapid business travel, a new generation of supersonic airliners is being planned. These aircraft will be quieter than Concorde, and able to carry twice as many passengers over distances of up to 13,000 km (8,000 miles). The costs will be so high that only an international consortium of companies will be able to afford to develop such an aircraft. Major airlines may prefer to see a new series of economical "superjumbo" jets, able to carry more passengers than ever before.

SPACE STATION

There are still plans to build a permanent space station, which would enable scientists in space to carry out experiments and study the Earth and the stars. It would also make it much simpler to repair damaged satellites, because engineers would travel from the space station rather than from the Earth.

Space station

With wings folded, HL-20 fits in Space Shuttle

Full-scale model of the HL-20

Andromeda Galaxy

SPACE TAXIS

If permanent space stations become a reality, small, economical space vehicles will be needed to ferry crews to and from the Earth. One such vehicle under development is the HL-20, a sort of scaled-down version of the Space Shuttle. Launched by an expendable booster, it would use its wings to make a normal runway landing. With its wings folded, this versatile craft would be small enough to be carried in the cargo bay of the main Space Shuttle if necessary.

INTERSTELLAR TRAVEL

Unfortunately, the galaxies, stars, and planets beyond our Solar System are so far away that it is doubtful whether we will ever be able to send astronauts to them. For example, the nearest star to the Earth is 4.2 light-years away. It is more likely that we will explore the Universe using robot spacecraft that will relay information back to Earth.

Experimental high-mileage cars

THE FUTURE OF THE CAR

Faced with dwindling energy supplies, the cars of the future will have to use less fuel and cause less pollution. This could be achieved by using lightweight materials, such as carbon-fibre and aluminium, to make smaller cars that will do more kilometres per litre of petrol. Electric cars are only a partial solution, because fossil fuels still have to be burned in power stations to make electricity to recharge the cars' batteries. Solar-powered cars may one day become viable in warm climates.

MORE POWER, MORE SPEED

Our obsession with speed shows no sign of waning. Record breakers such as Craig Breedlove and Richard Noble (*see* **MILESTONES 1965** *and* **1983**) aim to build supersonic cars that will reach speeds of 1,200 kph (745 mph) or more. Although some people consider this very wasteful, the lessons learned from such cars help designers to develop better cars for everyday use.

New tram system in Manchester, England

TRAMS REBORN

As city centres around the world become choked with traffic, many city authorities are building rapid-transport systems to lure people away from their cars and to free the streets of congestion.

Underground railways continue to play a vital role, but there are many new light railways being built, and in some cities trams are being reintroduced decades after they were withdrawn.

Richard Noble's *Thrust SSC* **supersonic car**

AN END TO COMMUTING?

One of the main reasons that people travel into city centres is to get to work. But changing work patterns may also change the face of city travel. Many more people are now working from home on computers, and using telephones, modems, and fax machines to communicate with their employers. Crowded commuter trains and buses, long delays, and traffic jams may one day be a thing of the past.

Working from home

SUPERCRUISERS

The enduring popularity of leisure cruises has prompted shipping companies to plan new, ever-larger cruise ships, some exceeding 100,000 tonnes. These "supercruisers" will offer all the usual luxuries, as well as high-tech facilities such as virtual reality theatre and retractable domes to cover on-deck swimming pools in bad weather.

This 100,000-tonne cruiser will be the biggest passenger ship ever built

Experimental Russian WIG

WING-IN-GROUND-EFFECT CRAFT

Jet airliners experience the "ground effect" as they land. A cushion of air trapped between the wings and the runway causes extra lift. "Wing-in-ground-effect" water craft (or WIGs) use this phenomenon to skim across the water on a cushion of air like a hovercraft – but they can travel much faster. WIGs are still in the developmental stage, but may one day provide rapid transport across lakes and between coastal islands.

NEW HULL DESIGNS

The future of fast sea transport may lie with SWATH (Small Water Area Twin Hull) vessels, which look like a cross between a catamaran and a hydrofoil. A SWATH vessel floats on two cigar-shaped pods below the waterline. The rest of the ship stands clear of the water on slim struts. Only the struts cut through the waves, enabling the ship to ride rough seas at high speed using less power than ships with normal hulls.

Artist's impression of the "Super Technoliner" SWATH cargo ship under development in Japan

Index

Emergency ambulance, 1990s

**"Deltic" Diesel-Electric
Locomotive, 1956**

Schweizer 300c
helicopter, 1980s

G-BSUP

Battery-powered car for disabled drivers, 1990s

Acknowledgements

Dorling Kindersley would like to thank:
The staff of the National Maritime Museum and the Science Museum; Esther Labi for editorial assistance; Robin Hunter and Kate Eagar for design help; Sarah Hill; British Museum Education Service; Museum of Mankind; Royal Institute of Natural Architects.

Key: l=left r= right c=centre t=top b=bottom or below a=above

Special Photography: Tina Chambers for photography at National Maritime Museum. David Exton and John Lepine for photography at the Science Museum.
Additional Photography: American Museum of Natural History (artefact 50/5756); Ashmolean Museum; British Library; British Museum; ESA; Exeter Maritime Museum; London Planetarium; Museum of Mankind/British Museum; National Maritime Museum; National Motor Museum, Beaulieu; National Railway Museum, York; Noordwijk Space Expo; The Royal Armouries, Royal Artillery Trust, Woolwich; Science Museum.
Photographers: Peter Anderson; Geoff Brightling; Martin Cameron; Peter Chadwick; Andy Crawford; Geoff Downs; Peter Downs; Mike Dunning; Lynton Gardiner; Philip Gatward; Christi Graham; Peter Hayman; Dudley Hubbard; Dave King; Richard Leeney; Ray Moller; Nick Nicholls; Susanna Price; James Stevenson; Clive Streeter; Matthew Ward; Jerry Young.
Illustrators: David Ashby 10cr; Russell Barnett 9tr, 9br, 12tl; Luciano Corbello 42tl, 42bl; David Pugh, 41t.
Picture Credits: Lesley & Roy Adkins 7crb; Advertising Archives 33cla; J.A. Allen & Co. Ltd/Major A.B. Shone 14cla; Archiv für Kunst und Geschichte 10bc, 26clb, 28br, 31bc, 33bc/Musée du Louvre 10tc
Arcwind Ltd 41cb; Ashmolean Museum, Oxford 9tc; Australian High Commission, London 40cl; Aviation Photographs International 34tl, 41tr, 43tr, 45tl; Aviation Picture Library/Austin Brown 33tc, 43tcb;; Stephen Piercey 34ca; Avico Press/Aleksander Belyaev 45bl; Photos courtesy of The Boeing Company 40tl, 41clb; Bridgeman Art Library/National Railway Museum, York 17bl; British Library 12tr, British Museum 6tl; Neill Bruce/ Peter Roberts Collection 26tr; Peter A. Clayton 6bla; Coo-ee Historical; Picture Library 32tr; Culver Pictures 19c; Devonshire Collection, Chatsworth. Reproduced by permission of the Chatsworth Settlement

Trustees 14cr; C.M. Dixon 6tr; ET Archive 6bra, 7bc, 14tr, 18cra, 21cla/Bibliotheque Nationale; Paris 12cr; British Museum 9c; Ironbridge Gorge Museum 17crb; Mary Evans 8tr, 8cr, 8crb, 11cra, 13tc, 13br, 14ca, 15tc, 15tr, 16tr, 16bc, 18tr, 20bc, 21cb, 22c, 23tc, 23bc, 24cr, 25bc, 27tl, 27bl, 27crb, 28clb, 28tr, 29ca, 29br, 30tl, 31cr, 32tc, 34bc; Werner Forman Archive/Nick Saunders 13tcr; Genesis Space Photo Library 35br, 37tr; Robert; Harding/Nelly Boyd 45cra; Wilbur House, Hull City Museum & Art Galleries 16crb; Hulton Deutsch Collection 15cb, 18clb, 24tr, 35bl, 39bc, 40br; Images Colour Library 43cb; Image Select 26tl; Imperial War Museum 34c; London Transport Museum 24cl, 30cla, 31cra, 32cla; Maclaren 39cl; Master & Fellows, Magdalene College, Cambridge 13c; Magnum/René Burri 43tl; Jean Gaumy 38cb; Mangar Aids Ltd 44cl; Mansell Collection 22tl, 23tl, 24crb, 25cb; Mercedes Benz 32cl, 36bc; Musée J.Armand Bombardier, Québec 34bl; NASA 40tr, 40tcb, 42tc, 42tr, 45tcr, 45tcl/JPL 36tc; National Maritime Museum 14bc; National Motor Museum, Beaulieu 38cra; National Museums of Scotland/Scottish Ethnological Archive 27clb; Peter Newark's Pictures 17cb, 24bc, 28cl, 30bc, 33c, 34cl, 34clb, 35cra, 35c; Nissan 41bc; Novosti 38bc; Robert Opie Collection 26br, 28bl; Pictor International 37crb, 42br; Pitt Rivers Museum 22-23c; Popperfoto 44crb; The Post Office 18cla; QA Photos 44br; Quadrant 30tc, 34cr, 36br, 38trb, 39cb, 42cr; Tony Hobbs 38tr; Range Pictures 23c, 26bc, 31crb, 38bl; Redfunnel 37bc; Rex Features 42cl; Ann Ronan at Image Select 16br, 19tr, 21tr; Royal Aeronautical Society 20tl, 24tl, 31tc, 33tr; Royal Navy Submarine Museum 15bc; Science Museum/Science & Society Picture Library 3bl, 8tl, 17tc, 18cl, 19crb, 21c, 21br, 23cl, 23tr, 23crb, 25tl, 27cr, 28tl, 29tc, 29cr, 35bra; Science Photo Library/Martin Bond 36cb; Tony Hallas 45tr; NASA 32bc; Sea Containers 44clb, 44cbl; Frank Spooner Pictures 43br, 44bl/Alain le Bot 45cl; Mitsuhiro Wada 44cb;Tony Stone Images 38cr/Warren Jacobs 43cra; Martin Rogers 41crb Technological Research Association of Techno-Superliner, Tokyo 45br; Transport Know How Ltd 41c; TRH/DOD 34cla; Westland 35bla; Triumph Motorcycles Ltd 44cr; Michael Turner 45c; University Museum of National Antiquities Oslo, Norway 11br; Westland Group 44tr; Noel Whittall 41tl; York Archaeological Trust 11bc.

East Indiaman, 17th century